For Donna —

Shades of the past are lingering in here — so we, in a way, share its intention —

Love

David

THE TRANSFORMING SELF

THE TRANSFORMING SELF

New Dimensions in Psychoanalytic Process

DAVID SHAINBERG, M.D.

Intercontinental Medical Book Corporation New York

Intercontinental Medical Book Corporation
381 Park Avenue South/New York, N. Y. 10016

Library of Congress Catalog Card No. 73-662
ISBN 0-913258-09-1
Printed in U.S.A.

ACKNOWLEDGMENTS

A number of sources from the literature have been referred to, each bibliographically cited at the pertinent point in the text. The author expresses particular thanks to the following authors, editors and publishers for their kind permission to quote verbatim from the copyrighted works listed below.

Gregory Bateson (Editor), *Perceval's Narrative: A Patient's Account of His Psychosis, 1830-1832* (Stanford: Stanford University Press, 1961; reprinted with permission of the publisher).

Anton Boisen, "The Form and Content of Schizophrenic Thinking," *Psychiatry,* 5 (1942), 23-33 (with permission of *Psychiatry: Journal of the Study of Interpersonal Processes*).

Malcolm Bowers, "The Onset of Psychosis–A Diary Account," *Psychiatry,* 28 (1965), 346-358 (with permission of *Psychiatry: Journal of the Study of Interpersonal Processes*).

Morag Coate, *Beyond All Reason* (Philadelphia: Lippincott, 1965; copyright © 1965 by Morag Coate, reprinted by permission of J. B. Lippincott Company).

David Cooper, *Psychiatry and Antipsychiatry* (London: Tavistock Publications Ltd., 1967; reprinted with permission of the publisher).

Paul Federn, excerpted from Chapter 10, "Ego Psychological Aspects of Schizophrenia," in Edoardo Weiss (Editor), *Ego Psychology and the Psychoses* (New York: Basic Books, 1952; © 1953 by Imago Publishing Co., Ltd., reprinted with permission of Basic Books, Inc.).

Joanne Greenberg, *I Never Promised You a Rose Garden* (New York: Holt, Rinehart and Winston, 1964; copyright © 1964 by Joanne Greenberg, reprinted by permission of Holt, Rinehart and Winston, Inc.).

Paul Hackett, *The Cardboard Giants* (New York: G.P. Putnam's Sons, 1952; reprinted with permission of the publisher).

Jay Haley, "The Family of a Schizophrenic: A Model System," *Journal of Nervous and Mental Diseases,* 129 (1959), 357 (© 1959 and with permission of The Williams & Wilkins Co., Baltimore).

"Finding the Real Self: A Letter with a Foreword by Karen Horney," *American Journal of Psychoanalysis*, 9 (1949), 3 (reprinted by permission of Helen A. DeRosis, M.D., Editor of *The American Journal of Psychoanalysis*).

Harold Kelman, *Helping People* (New York: Science House, 1971; reprinted with permission of the publisher).

Thomas Kuhn, "The Structure of Scientific Revolutions," in *The International Encyclopedia of Unified Science*, Vol. II, No. 2 (Chicago: University of Chicago Press, 1962; © and reprinted with permission of the publisher).

R. D. Laing, *The Politics of Experience* (London: Penguin Books, 1967; © 1967 by R. D. Laing, reprinted by permission of Penguin Books, Ltd.).

Jonathan Lang, "The Other Side of Hallucination," *American Journal of Psychiatry*, Part I, 94 (1938), 1089-1097; Part II, 96 (1939), 423-430.

Susanne Langer, *Mind: An Essay on Human Feeling*, Vol. I (Baltimore: Johns Hopkins University Press, 1967; with permission of the publisher).

H. Nash, "The Role of Metaphor in Psychological Theory," *Behavioral Science* 8 (1963), 336 (with permission of *Behavioral Science*).

Mara Selvini Palazzoli, excerpted from Chapter 9, "Anorexia Nervosa," in Silvano Arieti (Editor), *The World Biennial of Psychiatry and Psychotherapy* (New York: Basic Books, 1970; © 1970 by, and reprinted with permission of, Basic Books, Inc.).

K. H. Pribram, "The Neurophysiology of Remembering," *Scientific American,* 220 (1969), 76 (reprinted with permission of Scientific American, Inc.).

D. W. Winnicott, "Ego Distortion in Terms of True and False Self," in *The Maturational Processes and the Facilitating Environment* (London: Hogarth, 1965; reprinted with permission of The Hogarth Press, Ltd., and International Universities Press, New York).

Contents

PART I. THE FORMING PROCESS

PART II. THE CREATIVE THRUST

PART III. THE REVOLUTION AGAINST THE OLD FORM

Preface

During the years that I have worked on this book, there have been many influences contributing to its emergence. Of these, involvement with my patients has held first place. Their consistent attempts to find and express what was real about themselves have been an essential stimulus to discovering more about the direction and intentions of their life aspirations.

To Dr. Lewis R. Wolberg, Dean and Director Emeritus of Postgraduate Center for Mental Health, I owe very special thanks. In 1969 when my colleagues and I left the American Institute for Psychoanalysis, we were looking for a place to continue our work. Dr. Wolberg invited us to join him and his colleagues at the Postgraduate Center. In so doing, he provided the kind of open forum and stimulation for dialogue which has made it possible for me to work on and extend the ideas I have developed in this book.

In May 1972, when he heard me present "The Dilemma and the Challenge of Being Schizophrenic" at the Annual Meeting of the American Academy of Psychoanalysis in Dallas, Texas, Dr. Wolberg urged me to expand my ideas into a book. He read the manuscript at several stages and offered many useful suggestions. His help contributed greatly to the book's appearance.

The substantial influence of Dr. Harold Kelman will be apparent to readers. His theories of symbolizing, communing, and creative integrating have been major guides for what has emerged here. But these obvious contributions may obscure still another, of greater importance. Over the years, Dr. Kelman has been both a mentor and a friend, and has helped clarify many of the issues discussed here. He has done this both by being an example of the momentum of the self articulating and by illuminating moments of uncertainty and obscurity which continually gave way to moments of security and lucidity. His personal dedication to the process of self articulation and his beliefs in the capacity of the human organism to meet the struggles that make human development possible continue to be for me a source of support and assurance. Life and society offer many delays and detours. Often the pain of truth is great and all too frequently assuaged by self deception. Human beings need other human beings who will support rather than divert their engagement with the painful dilemmas of existence. I consider myself fortunate to have had my life immeasurably broadened and deepened by knowing and working with Dr. Harold Kelman.

My indebtedness to Karen Horney is also evident throughout the book. Her work asserts again and again the belief in the dynamic growth possibilities of all human beings. This book attempts to extend her ideas in the direction I feel she was pointing. Last, but hardly least, I am obviously in great debt to

Freud for establishing, among many other things, one of the main instruments by which I have been able to investigate the nature of this process.

To three other people I owe much:

John Briggs II's belief in the spirit of this book combined with his editorial skills helped to transform my idiosyncratic style into one which increased the possibilities for a greater contact with my readers. He helped me to see where I stood, what in my position needed to be questioned and clarified, and finally to be communicated with clarity. Out of our working together has developed an enduring friendship and a mutual commitment to the process of self articulation.

When first written, the book was essentially a theoretical map delineating main directions. The stimulating, cajoling, and sometimes violent confrontations with my novelist brother, Lawrence Shainberg, served to push me further inside the process. How far I have come I owe in a large measure to his insistence that language is a sacred tool, one which can be as deceptive as it can be beautiful.

My wife, Diane, a psychotherapist with a gift for understanding the inner spaces, has read the manuscript on many occasions. Her suggestions, support, and enthusiasm for the process articulated here contributed immeasurably as she communicated them with her own particular perceptiveness.

There have been others who have helped whom I cannot mention; the list is long and the delineation of what I took from them more difficult. But, as in any book which points to possibility for the human soul, there has been a general collaboration with many who share in being part of the larger Self experience that unites us all as partners in a process which extends from the past through the present and into the future.

David Shainberg, M.D.

TO MY STUDENTS AND COLLEAGUES AT
POSTGRADUATE CENTER FOR MENTAL HEALTH

Introduction

This book is about the struggle for self-realization.

We all hold deeply within us that eternal wish to have a life which is meaningful; that is, we hope we will find that we are glad we are alive and that what we do will give us a sense that we are connected to what we want in the world. We all know, at some level, that a meaningful life can occur only when we are restored to ourselves, to our being—and we have all had the experience of that, in a sense of love for another person, in a meeting with a child, in a sense of accomplishment from learning how to do something. Such experiences let us know that we have capacity and are connected to existence. Some would have it that this state of self is the right of every human being and that we are entitled to it. But, the reality of the human condition is that the self can only be realized in a struggle against immense forces, both internal and external. The inner forces are difficult to spot because of our intense involvement in our delusions: the outer forces arise from society, and from people who are absorbed in delusions of their own. There are those who believe that it is important to learn to live in society first. But this avoids the obvious fact that it is only when one can participate and live from his own center, his own self, that he can participate with other human centers, for the greater benefit and growth of all.

Mental illness, schizophrenia, borderline phenomena, and neurotic situations are all forms of self-organization which, to a greater or lesser degree, preclude the open, free participation in the forming process which is the self in the state of realizing itself. Forming is the play of life as it is manifested in nature, in organisms unfolding and expressing their flow of being in the universe. Mental illnesses can be seen as plans of behavior which organize the novelty of life into forms that provide a specious safety rather than allowing the organism to freely explore its capacity to engage in the uncertainties, possibilities and paradoxes of existence. Mental illnesses are, thus, the more obvious manifestations of the general human tendency to obstruct self-realization. There is obviously something about the human condition which involves the need to fix things in rigid forms. Constantly we see how people form themselves (or rather, fix themselves) around goals they hope will keep them invulnerable to the uncertainties of change. They cling to prestige, power, money, speed, efficiency and forms, as the schizophrenic person clings to his alienation. Indeed, the clinging to such things alienates these "sane" people, too.

Just how it is that a person begins to change is not clear. We know some novelties break through and an individual realizes he has new possibilities for a larger way of living. He may get physically ill and see in that the fact of human death; he may then see that it is time for him to think about how he wants to live his life, time to stop obscuring himself in his fears and his need to please everyone around him. Or, he may meet a man—and there are always a few on the planet at any one time—who has lived his life in truth and commitment to self, may be impressed by the joy in living which emanates from such a person, may come to see the drabness in his own existence in comparison and be stimulated to new development. Or he may become aware of new possibilities through art or literature. In whatever way the possibility for new experiencing makes itself evident, the person in transformation begins to wonder about the rigidity of his present form and begins to feel uncomfortable with the sterility and automaticity of his way of life.

When the person actually challenges the old form, there are doubts and despairs. He is perhaps sad over what he has missed and depressed about having to face the task of changing himself with so few assets. In this book, I have tried to show that each time anyone confronts novelty and his own new feelings and experience for exploring and relating to the world, he exercises his being. Through these confrontations, there is an accrual of capacities for further engagement. I have called this process self-articulation. It occurs through making connections to the various aspects of the self, to the past, the present, the future, to feelings, thoughts, dreams, and images as they manifest an engagement in the now. By making these connections, one builds the muscles of being much as an athlete builds his strength in daily workouts. The self emerges out of this exercise.

It seemed to me as I re-read this book in final manuscript that both my experience of writing it, and the experience I think readers will have in reading it, mirror the process of self-realization I am attempting to describe. I think the book may be said to emerge gradually into the possibility, in the way we see self-realization emerge. In the unfolding, the reader will see that each beginning does not mean a complete realization. There are small and large setbacks whenever there are threats by the new system to the old. The examples in the book portray the intimations and real moments of self-expression and self-clarification. These come about through the patient's associations, symbolizations, connections, focusings and recapitulations. The book, too, uses these modes to bring itself into being.

In each chapter I had the impulse to show the complete process, since in each stage of that process there are phases of doubt and depressions, exhilaration and conflict about giving up older and supposedly safer patterns of being in favor of new, uncertain ones. Then, too, each occurrence of the process is a separate, unique instance of its organic—not logical—unfolding. Of course, to have repeated the whole process each time would have made the book intolerably long and redundant. Still, it should be clear that, as ontology recapitulates phylogeny, the process of each new development repeats the overall process of development and points the way to future development. The words and phrases I have used to define this development—"incipient processes", "revolution", "immersion", even "self-articulation" itself—should be thought of rather metaphorically as descriptions of hard-to-identify transitional states of forming.

In a sense, one must perhaps read the whole book to grasp the essence of the idea I have tried to convey. This is because the essence of that idea is process itself. As an individual makes more and more connections to his authentic self in his ongoing experience in reality, he increases his relationship to the world. As he is more connected to himself, he becomes more a flow of patterns in the world and, consequently, more of a self functioning in a multi-dimensional universe. He is thereby more of an autonomous entity. So perhaps the book, like the very process of self-realization, is one of cumulative effect toward establishing its subject.

Finally, it has been one of my main goals here to clarify the role of the psychoanalyst. The central value of any psychoanalytic therapy is self-realization. There are those therapies which propose to be supportive, but even here we must hope that the goal is to prepare the patient to get ready for self-realization, or, at least, to help him be appreciative of how the disruptions he is facing are the result of his having begun to seek experience beyond the confines of his limited form. In this, a patient undergoes anxiety, and the support of the therapist is, hopefully, aimed at encouraging him to continue to experience this anxiety. In the book I have pointed out the ways I feel this can be done. There are many places where a crucial support for the anxiety of uncertainty can help a patient endure the pain he must endure if he is to grow.

Thus, I hope this book can contribute, in some measure, to preventing blocks on the part of psychoanalysts or other friends to those who would like to move out of the prisons of their darkening fear and into the inner and outer and brighter world of self.

Part I
THE FORMING PROCESS

CHAPTER 1

Transforming

In analytic sessions I have often been impressed with the biological process of one person's talking to another, and disorder becoming order. This process is miraculous and real, but so common that we forget how fantastic an event it is. A patient will talk of all that he is feeling. He talks from *inside* an event only after he talks *about* the event; in this he begins to experience the feelings he had when he was *in* the event, and talking becomes an event and an alive action itself. Following such sessions, patients will often feel a strong sense of self.

MRS. M.

One woman, Mrs. M., came to her analytic session a bit late. This was unusual as she was always punctual, though breathlessly so. This day, she was three minutes late and began her session with the statement that she was afraid I would give her a "rapping on the wrist" for her tardiness. As she progressed in the analytic hour, she interwove her comments about this fear around thoughts about her fear of being criticized by others in other interpersonal relations and her anger at feeling this fear. She also spoke of her self-criticism. Then she went on to describe feelings of being able to do without others and of being able to be sometimes unconcerned about their approval. This was, she said, a new feeling for her. She noted that she was more and more able to spend time on her own, and the Sunday before she had been entirely alone. I did not speak during the session and the next day she reported:

> After yesterday's session, I felt my feet were on the ground as I walked down the street. I did not have a destination as I walked, but I had the very definite feeling that I did not need one, I could go where my feet would take me.

Mrs. M. feels she is being criticized. She often feels criticized; it is her usual mode of forming her experience. In a state of uncertainty, not keeping to the minute of the hour, Mrs. M. organizes, as usual, around this form of being criticized. Such a form she "thinks" enables her to "clarify" her situation, to integrate it. The active experiencing and struggle in the session involves her clarification of the workings of this forming process as it appears in other aspects of her life. She speaks of feeling criticized and coerced by others. She sees how this has made her into an object being observed by other subjects in the world. She outlines this pattern of herself and, as such, works out what her experience of being in uncertainty is. As the session evolves. the creative process of integrating brings her mysteriously to a new organization, one of being able, for a moment at least, to face the uncertainty she meets in reality: "I did not have a destination as I walked, but I had the very definite feeling that I did not need one." This new state is a transformation. Through seeing what she previously did with uncertainty, she now moves to be more open to that uncertainty. In this state, she is ready to experience whatever she finds in her reality, and, thus, is involved in a process in which living is a more active and open ordering. For the moment, at least, she has ceased to be an object worked over (criticized) by subjects. She has become a form of a flowing pattern of connections rather than a form separate-subject-and-object, split and alienated from herself.

Importantly, Mrs. M. is able to undergo this transformation because she actively engages in the process of the session, by actively, not passively, *participating.*

The biological nature of participation in transforming process is illustrated by the data on imprinting which has appeared in the ethological literature. Eckhard Hess[1] has observed that at an optimum time of 13 to 16 hours after hatching, wild mallard ducklings can be imprinted to follow a decoy. They will invariably follow this fake model of a mother whenever a sound similar to that of the mother is connected to the man-made form. *But imprinting occurs only if the ducks are permitted actually to move after the object.* Learning occurs only when there is an active participation and involvement of the total body musculature; only, that is, when the organism is involved *directly* in the process. This suggests that the connection of functions is essential in learning. There is not a subject which is reflecting or absorbing an object. There is a unifying, subject as object, a totality that comes into being ultimately through the establishment of connections between the muscles which move in their relation to the duckling's perceptions of the changes in the relationship between it and the model. In other words, learning is the organization of a whole, which is subject and object as one.

Another example in this vein comes from the experiments of Richard Held[2] who fitted subjects with prism eyeglasses which overturned and reversed their vision in order to find out how they would adapt to this sensory displacement. He found that the subjects could adapt best when the visual experience was accompanied by motor activity, when they were allowed to move around on their own. But when the subjects were wheeled about in wheelchairs, their adaptation was much slower. It was obviously necessary for Held's subjects to have what neurologists refer to as "reafference", a feedback from the muscles as they attempt to orient in the world of experience. This reafference permits coordination of the visual motor and kinesthetic processes of the total system. The subjects had to move and to act for themselves, to create an interaction event which would allow them to achieve an order in their world.

From other patients, after sessions like the one with Mrs. M., I have heard such statements as:

> I felt I could handle what came and did not panic. In fact, I felt quite calm and serious as I listened to what my friend said about the errors I had made.
>
> I sensed that I could try. I knew what I had done was inadequate and not very good, but I was not thrown by it . . .
>
> I tried it, but I did not do so well. Next time I think I can do better.

Each of these statements suggests there has been an emergence around a new view of self. The sessions which produced these statements and their concomitant events can be considered kinds of experiments similar to the ones developed by Held. The patients begin operating, so to speak, with new glasses, engaging the uncertainty they feel in the open situation of the analytic process. I had "promised" by the virtue of the analytic situations that I would be there to help them if they needed help; but they were encouraged by my silence or words to help themselves. The old view of self was such that they could not trust their own spontaneous efforts to organize. With the new glasses they learn to look for the new possibilities and actively engage in the anxiety of uncertainty. This approach allows them to explore different perspectives and make different connections which they live out in a process of being with themselves, with me, and in the world. All this activity leads to a feedback or reafference: they discover that they can be in the world with the assets and capacities they have as features of what they are. They do not have to be anything more than what they are. This discovery leads to a further reafference in the form of greater self-confidence. Thereafter, the feedback of any errors they make can serve as clues for how to change rather than as evidence that they are "bad" people. This is an important difference in form. Everything that happens in the flow of the life that they live after developing this new attitude of self is seen differently. They are different in the way they order their experience.

ORDERING

Order manifests itself in a number of ways,[3] more than could ever be listed. There is order in nature's seasonal cycle, in the diurnal variation, and the regularity of development. It is in the assembling of the words on a page and of the letters in the words. It is my hands on the typewriter and the shape of my hands. It is the shape a person has, the color of his hair, the form of his nose. All these represent the presence of order in nature. The regulation of the body, the careful feedback of the glands are order-in-process. Order is not something which is separate and imposed: it emerges as functioning coherence. Lwoff[4] writes:

> . . . order is the fixed arrangement present in the existing constitution of things. Order may also be considered as a sequence of succession in space or time. Biological order is all that and it is especially a sequence in space *and* time. Biological order is dual, structural and functional, static and dynamic. Structural and functional orders are the complementary aspects of the living being.

The problem in our understanding of order is our difficulty in comprehending structure and function as *ordering-in-process*. We look at change as a something which can be defined.[5] We give relative stabilities names and then consider ourselves to be defining fixed structures which persist in time. We miss, in this, the continual activity of the creation of structure. Then we compound our self-deception, elaborating our ideas of staticity by our emphasis on the dynamic interactions of the parts which make up the entities which we have previously defined. Cause and effect thinking emerges from this position.[6] And the conceptual result of this position is the separation of subject and object. We claim they make up two separate and supposedly well-defined stabilities or equilibria. Further, and perhaps most devastatingly, we create a separation in our thinking about thinking as well. We consider knowing to be our reception of what is arriving to us from the outside the self. This leads us to believe that order is a given which we passively receive from nature. An object, accordingly, is considered to exist in some defined state of order which we merely record with camera-like senses.[7]

The separation of subject and object is a rigidified and limited approach to understanding our place in reality. *Because, in fact, we always feel ourselves as part of flow.* We do not feel ourselves as boxes which simply register the pellets of perception that bounce off of us. We know ourselves as part of many processes which influence what we are feeling in any situation. We know that even our vision can be distorted by changes in our moods and our emotional states. Our organism is, in fact, a hierarchy of systems shifting and forming its connections as a part of the universe and as a function of its phylogenetic and ontogenetic processes.[8] All of this is so complex it defies the imagination. But we know that there are constant shifts, that any perception, or knowing, is created in a process which is the history of the former (the one who forms), his current state, the state of what he sees, their relationship to each other, and to others, etc., etc., etc. The shaping and reshaping of forms is the forming process. When we appreciate this fact, we can see that the usual static notions of ordering and form are extremely limited. The experiments of Held and Hess demonstrate the complexity of this open ordering called forming.[9,10]

The work of Piaget,[11] Bruner,[12] and other developmental psychologists has illuminated the processing activity which a child moves through in his comprehension of being in the world. This work has shown that a child does not simply register that there are objects in the world. Rather, he moves through stages of discovering himself in interaction with objects, as a connecting effective agent.

Piaget shows, for example, that a child learns to draw, at first, by simply moving the pencil in a random way which apparently reflects his changing internal state. If the child is looking at an object, his random movement will show some vague connection to this outside "object". Then at a certain age, the child actually begins to notice a resemblance between his connecting (his drawing) and the rectangle that is "over there". He becomes interested. He begins to sharpen up his internal impression and then the lines on the page. First corners are introduced and then the lines are straightened out, made perpendicular and so on. Order is created by the steady interacting of both the child and object perceived. This is a function of the unity that is the unity child-object relating event. In the transforming, there is the creation of a new order of all connections: it is clear that this process is not a passive registration.

Mrs. M. was organizing her anxiety into two polarized units and thus did not, so she thought, have to really deal with the uncertainty she experienced. She had been in anxiety with the uncertainty. The outside me was "rapping her on the wrists" much as Piaget's children are affected by the sight of the object. As she experienced her connection to herself, to me, and to others, she sharpened her perception of her relating process. She then dealt more accurately with the facts of the world–like a child learning to reproduce right angles in its drawings.

PSYCHOANALYSIS AND SUBJECT-OBJECT THINKING

In psychoanalytic theory, subject-object thinking is perpetuated in the constructs of "secondary" and "primary process thinking". Freud[13] regarded the subject and the object as two different kinds of mental events belonging to two different systems, the conscious and the unconscious, and later, the ego and the id. This distinction coincided with his idea that logical and non-logical thought processes belong to two unconnected systems of organization. "Secondary" thought is a reality-oriented system. It is grounded in a reality which is asserted to be fixed and secondary process is assumed to be the proper relationship of the self to the world. It is the organism *passively* "able" to perceive what is "out there". A thought in the mind is connected to a perceptual image which springs into the head as reality: that correspondence is described as "true". "Primary" process is characterized formally by Freud as including displacement, condensation, and symbolism. It is a form characteristic of sleeping states as seen in reported dreams and in the autistic paleologic of the schizophrenic. It is also characteristic of certain repressed forms which appear in psychoanalytic treatment. According to Freud's early formulations, some of which he later changed, the id, the system which characteristically uses the primary process, does not develop, and the primary process's appearance always indicates a form of regression to infantile organization.[14,15,16]

We can see that this view of the activity of thinking is wanting. Freud and his colleagues focused on the *contents* (or static orders) of their patients' thought processes. But the *functional* aspects of thinking reveals something else. For example, study of creative process shows that there are different forms of thinking involved in creativity. Arieti[17] has defined a "tertiary process" as characteristic of creativity. He claims there is a combination of the primary type thinking and the secondary logical connections which reach out beyond the limits of both. The study of children's play also broadens our understanding of non-logical thought processes. Galenson[18] has reported that children's play evolves through different stages. The ways a child organizes his play indicate a non-logical form of relating; he moves through a processing of these forms, *creating autonomy by his capacity to separate and form his position in space.* He does all of this with "non-logical" thought. He uses a kind of presentational symbolism which Susanne Langer[19] has described. This symbolism presents events in a simultaneous pattern so that the information value is derived from the organization and spatial patterning of the forms that are laid out. The meanings of this array of forms depends on the totality of the presentation. Langer writes:

> The meanings given through language are successively understood, and gathered into a whole by the process called discourse; the meanings of all other symbolic elements that compose a larger, articulate, symbol are understood only through the meaning of the whole, through their relations with the total structure. Their very functioning as symbols depends on the fact that they are involved in a simultaneous, integral presentation.

Finally, our study of dreaming has taught us that the act of dreaming does not merely indicate a return to infantile forms. Dreams are known to be active integrating processes in which the thought forms, again like the presentational symbolism of Langer, are attempts to incorporate information about the self-in-action into the different organizational systems.[20] The forming which we see occurring in dreams does not follow a "logical" plan. In psychoanalytic process we often see the development of patient's dream thoughts, non-logical forming, into more complex and interrelated forms and we rightly take this to be a sign of progress.

Out of this there emerges, then, a new paradigm about the ordering of our thinking: all thinking is a form of knowing and is an *active process*. The division into primary and secondary process is a misleading and inadequate conceptualization. Thinking is a unitary function which employs many different modes of forming[21,22,23,24,25,26,27]: it is an operation of the integrating process, an ordering and the principal aspect of our presence in the universe. *Thinking represents an activity, not a reflection of reality. As such, it is never separate but always part of the total organism.*

The linguistic term "semiotic function" perhaps conveys the distinction for which I am striving here. Semiotic behavior is an organism's ability to represent something by a sign or a symbol or other object. One can also act to order his existence by the use of what Piaget calls "deferred imitation", drawing, painting, modeling, and mental imagery. In all these ways, the diverse uncertainties of individual existence are comprehended by the individual's operating functions. The forms that we see or hear as well are the result of the overall capacity—perceptually, cognitively, conatively, and biologically which the organism is using to integrate with the fixed and changing givens of the universe as a whole. Piaget[28] has noticed that the different modes of operation follow a basic logic of intelligence. This includes the logic of inclusion, a logic of ordering, and certain logics of correspondence. I would include all these as aspects of the process of forming: ordering is knowing.

THE MYSTERY OF OPENNESS

In literature, the mysterious ordering process and creative leap is illustrated in the traditional story of the prodigal son. He is one who experiences and gets involved in the process of life. He does not become a rigid structure, and, as a result, is depicted as stronger and more integrated.

In Shakespeare's *Henry IV, Part One*, Prince Hal emerges as a stronger figure than his nemesis, Hotspur. This is because Hotspur is part of the conventional structure while Hal, despite his father's admonitions that he is the heir apparent and should follow the royal path, joins Falstaff and engages in all that life has to offer. Having refused to live the limited existence of a Crown Prince, he comes to the throne with a strength and freedom not available to those who have conformed to the strict rules of royalty. Hal's values, beliefs, and judgments are subsequently shown by Shakespeare to be integrally connected to a sense of his nation's values, beliefs, and judgments. Hal is a structure, connected to his actions; he has evolved through trial and error, has learned anxiety and pain, and knows of England from the "people"—from his living *inside* his situation rather than following a set of ordinances supplied him from outside. Put another way, rather than be an object, a King, Hal becomes a subject like his people. This makes possible his later merging of subject and object just as Mrs. M.'s exploration of her experience in the session made possible her later sense of involvement.

Prince Hal seems to have a capacity to deal with the novel and the uncertain. Having grasped and lived through the process of life, he knows what is and is not part of Existence. He knows from his experience what can be prevented and what is part of the unavoidable pain of life. He does not pretend or lament when disaster or dilemma strikes. Analysts often hear patients speak in awe of people who can find their way in the world without concepts, education, and books: such legendary self-sufficient figures as the woodsman or trapper; the fisherman who can handle the big, overwhelming, and unexpected catch in the midst of the turbulence of the sea. In literature, again, the clown or fool is often depicted as one who can live in dissociation and who is the wiser for it (as is Lear's fool). Such are people who are able to be in reality, to be in the flow of change that is reality. They indicate a capacity for ordering. They indicate an ability to live in the unknown and be involved in ordering at their own levels of strength. We often speak admiringly of people who can live within their limitations and own the difficulties of whatever stress they encounter. Each system contains possibilities and ways in which it can handle and order new information. The capacities for ordering *develop*, as Prince Hal and Mrs. M. demonstrate, in an ongoing activity, whether it is one session or the course of a life. A person who has been through the experiences of the unknown learns to engage in the act of processing. He generalizes and orders with behavior inherent to himself. He learns through experience that uncertainty will become ordered through his engaging in the vicissitudes of failure and success. He learns to endure what we call "creative anxiety".

CONCLUSION

John Platt[29] defines two types of knowledge: scientific and cybernetic. The former is our understanding of regularity; it permits our indulgence in prediction. The latter is our understanding of the means and ends of existence: it is our subtle comprehension of the relationship between the resources available and the needs of any given event. It is the tennis player's capacity to judge the ball as it comes over the net. To the degree that he can play the ball and harmoniously relate to the way the ball plays him, he knows cybernetically. He organizes himself in the situation by incorporating the facticity of the ball and the possibilities he has for returning it. He may have to vary his shot when he sees the other player move on the other side of the net and, as he includes the feeling of the other's body motions, he moves in such and such a way. There is a constant process of intent, action, feedback, testing new action, and attempting to integrate the ball on his own stroke as the other's position and possibility of changing position develops. As anyone who has ever tried to master a sport can verify, the mastery is beyond any capacity to control. The emergence of the structure which can smoothly coordinate the multiplicity of the events involved is a matter of much more than trial and error. In fact, the very best players have usually begun when they were very young, at a time when structure could evolve freely. The older the person, the more structural patterns have developed and these block the capacity to shift to new systems or positions when necessary.

What specifically is the process of the change and reorganization? Before the session with Mrs. M., I observed that she was operating with an image of self which saw personal imperfection in a specific shape. Many patients berate themselves and are intolerant of their own errors. Actions in the world have to fit a preconceived notion. Such people are like machines, often very subtle ones, doing what they say they want while, in reality, they are imitating everyone around them; they are following a plan to contain uncertainty. The very process of this behavior, the self-hate, becomes an act of intolerance against any action that is incomplete or imperfect. When and if they register that an act or state does not match their plan, they attempt to bring the event or feeling into a coordination with the plan. These patients cannot bear the anxiety that goes with anything that does not fit the plan, though this moment of anxiety is necessary if they are to be creative. As we saw, Mrs. M. experienced such anxiety in our session followed by a burst of creativity which, for her, was rare. Ordinarily in obsessive patients, there is a tendency to dwell on the "what I should have done". This way of being focuses on remaining the same. Similar observations can be made about the patient who is driven by the need for recognition. He looks to complete a circle so that he does not have to face a situation he cannot control.

Important questions are embedded in these issues. What is it that leads people to resist the engagement of the unknown? What prevents the participation in the active process of knowing? What blocks the exploration of reordering in the spontaneous and creative possibilities that a new event offers? How do these blocks develop? How do they manifest themselves? How can an analyst help to encourage increased tolerance for anxiety?

CHAPTER 2

How the Former Forms: The Biological Foundation

The biological aspects of forming process remain among the central puzzles of scientific research. Biologically and psychologically, the question of the nature of form is essentially a question about the nature of mind relating to reality, of "minding"[1] in operation. Obviously, in one chapter it would be impossible to discuss or draw all the possible implications from the wide range of the work being done in the area of biological research, but it will be useful to suggest here the outlines of the issues and dilemmas.

BACKGROUND OF BIOPHYSICAL AND PSYCHOLOGICAL THEORIES OF FORMING

During Freud's time, the conception of nature, matter, force, and the nervous system arose out of the Newtonian world view. In this view, matter was a fact, or an extension, on which forces acted, but matter was an extension which could also produce forces. Newton introduced the idea that forces can act at a distance on matter and in an agent-like fashion can contribute to whatever forming process. Freud's ideas clearly relied on these views of the nature of reality.[2]

Holt,[3] leaning heavily on Amacher, has reviewed some of Freud's biological assumptions and pointed out the influences of his education. Brucke, Meynert, and Exner, Freud's three most influential instructors in the basic sciences, were members of what Bernfeld called "the School of Helmholtz", which, with its doctrine of physicalistic psychology, was "an attempt to overthrow the preceding Naturphilosophie and vitalism by rigorous attempts to treat the organism as a *physical system*"[4] (italics mine). The physiologists of the nineteenth century believed the nervous system functioned by carrying energy bundles from the afferent nerve endings. Any psychological process had to be paralleled to this physical process conceived as a one-to-one model. In the "Project", Freud hoped "to represent psychical processes as quantitatively determined states of specifiable material particles".[5] The nervous system was not thought to originate any activity, but it was believed all movements resulted from reflex arcs and responses to external pressure. That is to say, the organism was believed to be a "passive instrument which remained in a state of rest until stimulated, whereupon it functioned so as to rid itself of the incoming exogenous energies"[6] "Quantities of energy entered the system from two sources: the sensory organs and from the somatic element itself–endogenous stimuli which call equally for discharge. These have their origin in the cells of the body and give rise to the major needs, hunger, respiration, and sexuality".[7] Freud thought the behavior of the nervous system was organized to keep itself free of stimuli; motivation was then "a matter of the reduction of tensions or energic inputs".[8] This led to the idea of the organism as a helpless creature "threatened by the enormous energies in the external world".[9] External reality was conceived of as a dangerous agent of energy either acting at a distance or battering up directly against the poor human organism.

It is important to remember that during the nineteenth century, the classic laws of thermodynamics were applied indiscriminately to all living systems without attention to the differences between closed and open systems. Thus, the human organism was thought of as having fixed amounts of energy which were transformed within the container of the system from one shape to another. As Holt says, "it was natural for Freud to adopt as a first approximation the assumption of a fixed amount of libido, reverberating around within a closed system so that the fate of quantities could be traced. . . ."[10] In a closed, insulated system, the law of entropy applies. Such systems move toward death, decay, and repetition, and all these ideas appear in Freud's later psychodynamic formulations.

CURRENT THEORIES

Research data of the past seventy-five years have shown that the nineteenth century paradigm of the nature of biological organism is false. The nervous system is seen now to be an active, connecting, integrating function. There is much evidence to substantiate this fact. Among this are the numerous discoveries of so called biological clocks which organize organisms' behavior.[11] Hormonal cycles are now known to be connected to active neurochemical structures such as the neurohypophysis; this teaches us about structural-chemical functional integration. Recordings from various parts of the resting nervous system have long been known to exhibit a constant pulsation which would indicate the constant activity of the system.[12] The heart beat, respiration, and the sleep cycle are also indicative of the active integrating function of the nervous system.[13] Lastly, there has been an abundance of data in the last few years demonstrating that the central nervous system is always sending out impulses which influence the receptor's view of the external world. This crucial function governs the what and the how of the living organism in its transaction with the world.[14,15]

All of this data could be multiplied but the point is clear: the nervous system has been found to be *active*. In the light of this, reflex psychology, putting a stimulus into the box and retrieving a pre-established response over preset pathways moving from the surface to the effector muscle, seems a highly inadequate model for understanding any natural organism.[16,17,18] We have learned now that the way any stimulus is received is intimately dependent on the form of the internal process at the moment the event occurs. At any given moment, the organism has a shape, which is its relations in the world. If the organism registers a stimulus, it does so only as a result of the *kind* of shape it is, that is, as the kind of receptor it is. The shape is the unity of the active connecting system. It is a whole and, as such, will change if any of its subsystems is changed.

The paradigm of the organism as form and as forming is a view of biology quite different from that which considers each system as a separate entity or agent of a cause. Nature has been shown to be a field of forms in which all biological forms, mental and physical, are only temporary wholes, relative constancies. Even the word "nature" comes from the Latin root meaning "that which is being born", while the Greek word "physis" is based on a verb meaning "to grow". David Bohm, a theoretical physicist, writes: "reality may be likened to the flowing movement of a stream, producing eternally changing forms, such as vortices, ripples, waves, etc."[19]

Any element of nature, a mind, a thought, a person, a tree, or a mode of behavior, is essentially a temporary form turned up in the flowing process of change and activity. When we name an agent, a cause, or an effect, we are admitting our ignorance and our laziness which prevents us from seeing the multiple connections leading to this transient change in the relationships of a whole.

PERCEPTUAL FORMING

Contrary to the nineteenth century view of the nervous system, it has been found there are two types of neuro-electric activity in the brain instead of one![20] The nervous system had been believed to have only direct transmission in which impulses traveled down axons and crossed synapses and most understanding of behavior of human systems has been based on this model. Cathartic relieving of energy blocks, stimulus-response psychology and so on have evolved from these conceptions of the brain transmission. It has now been discovered there is another exceedingly more complicated and subtle form of activity in the nervous system, called ephaptic transmission. In ephaptic transmission, there are graded, slow potentials which oscillate locally in the brain tissue and are sensitive to many influences, including that of the local chemical environment. The slow potentials produce patterns which tend to organize the neighboring interactions as well as influence temporal aspects of the system. In these emerging, slow wave functions, we can describe states or backgrounds of integration which can be seen to have a microstructure. These ephaptic events are integrated with the synaptic transmission at junctions to form a further level of patterning. Thus, we have a shifting network of transmission which is constantly vacillating according to changes in the relationships with the organism itself and in the transactional process of organism in world. According to this system, then, the organism does not operate as a static structure; it is a form with temporary equilibrium states.

But Beurle notes that *without form equilibrium states would be unstable* and that one would soon find that "the activity has died away in some places and flared up in others. It is for this reason that activity with some form of spatial and temporal organization will always be favored".[21]

In the sensory mechanisms of the nervous system, there is another action which could be described as the development of form. Often when there is localized excitation, there is a surrounding inhibition of nerve conduction. This distinction provides a contrast between the two areas. This contrast is a form and the appearance of such a form allows for the polarization between this form and another different form in the brain. This is a communication inside the system. The form also is the beginning of the logic of the coding process in the nervous system. The next level of transmission is a relay of the contrast information. This action of the nervous system is the activity of abstracting. For example, in the visual system, retinal ganglion cells respond only to the contrast in excitations in the primary receptors of the eye. The ganglion abstracts the information in the form of excitation *relationships* in the primary cells and sends this information to the brain.[22,23]

In this connection, one of the most interesting and most important demonstrations of form in the nervous system is found in the work on the eye of the frog by Lettvin, Maturana, McCulloch, and Pitts.[24] The experimenters arranged to stimulate only one eye of the immobilized frog. The frog's eye was at the center of an artificial hemisphere with a radius of seven inches; they were able to place small objects on the inner surface of this hemisphere and move them around by magnets. Meanwhile, the researchers had implanted electrodes in the frog's optic nerve in order to measure "what the frog's eye tells the frog's brain". They studied the relationship between the impulse they recorded and the objects they were presenting. Obviously, it was possible to present virtually infinite numbers of patterns to the frog.

The researchers noted that the frog only responded to four kinds of forms. Lettvin and his colleagues named these: contrast detectors, moving edge detectors, net dimming detectors, and net convexity detectors.

Contrast detectors permit understanding of differentiation in environmental polarities. Moving edge detectors orient the frog's system to the flow of pattern relationships, while net dimming detectors would help it be aware of changes in light and any hovering forms (such as predators) which interrupt the form of the current relationship to reality. Net convexity detectors do not respond to changes in light or contrast but to small, dark objects when they move closer to the frog. It is the form evolution has developed for the frog to capture flying bugs, a system which abstracts this special information.

Such feature detectors and abstracting principles have been discovered in higher animals by Hubel and Wiesel.[25] They found that in kittens, from the retina to the cortex there is a hierarchical processing with successive, increasingly specific spatio-temporal patterns required for excitation. The visual cortex is organized to respond to straight and parallel lines because the input channels from the retinal ganglion cells are arranged in certain forms. In certain cells in the cortex, responsivity only occurs if the stimulus is oriented in a certain direction, with the termination of a line at one or both of its ends. Other groups of cells respond only if the line has a certain orientation and length, but the position is not important. The cortical response represents an abstraction from the retinal principles of operation. In the retina the stimulus light must be in contrast to the background and the response was found not to vary so long as the *relationship* between the light and dark was kept constant. This is the "form" in the response and is an example of forming-in-action. Each level of functioning in all the sensory systems studied thus far shows that the forming process serves to reduce redundancy in input and clarify certain relationships which apparently have been "discovered" in evolution to be important.[26]

SYSTEM EXPECTATIONS

How this all happens and how it develops is unclear. Held's work (Chapter 1) would indicate that *the operation of forms and forming emerges from the total kinesthetic operation of the organism*. Research has shown that if kittens are exposed experimentally only to vertical stripes, they do not develop horizontal detectors, and if exposed only to horizontal stripes, do not develop vertical detectors.[27]

We know that the eyeball is constantly moving in visual perception.[28,29] If this movement is prevented by stabilization of the eyeball, perception ceases. Acts of vision are, then, evolving from ongoing effort in which a coordination of behavior needs with the perceptual system is a constant process. Perhaps it is that the feedback of trial and error is led on by and directed by genetically adaptive systems which abstract the form and features that have been found necessary for functioning.

John Platt[30] has pointed out that pattern-organizing processes are part of a continual scanning by the perceptual apparatus. More particularly, he notes that we develop our idea of the way things are through a search for invariances. For instance, we look at one end of a line and have an experience. The aspect of the line at the other end falls on the same retinal cells and our unconscious inference is that this is a straightness. In effect, perceptually we are always comparing and reorienting ourselves according to our expectations. This reorientation is accomplished by active scanning which results in the learning of relationships through the "satisfaction" of feedback of connections which have been repeated. Objective reality or experience of relationships becomes, through learning, *secondary* to these features which have developed as guiding forms within the organism.

Lashley's famous Hixon symposium paper,[31] "The Problem of Serial Order in Behavior", has pointed out that it is impossible for there to be any organized orderly sequence of action without there being some form of matrix or representation built up in previous encounters with the environment. This matrix form, he insists, must be relatively resistant to changes on the basis of the immediate peripheral stimulations.

A further illustration of how learning affects behavior and how this is related to intentionality is the experiment of Pribram. Pribram[32] taught monkeys to distinguish between the right and left sides of a translucent panel. The scientists projected circles on the panel and if the monkey pressed the right half of the panel, it was rewarded with a peanut; it was similarly rewarded if it pressed the left side of the panel when stripes appeared. Electrodes had been placed in the visual cortex and recordings were made. The investigators expected the recorded waves would indicate what the monkey was seeing and that this would be different before learning and after. But they emphasize:

> What we did not expect was that we would be able to tell from the wave form whether the monkey saw a circle or a vertical stripe, whether he responded correctly or made a mistake and most surprising of all, whether he *intended* to press the right half or the left half of the panel once he was presented with the problem and *before* he initiated the response. All these differing electrical responses arose in the visual cortex, the part of the brain that receives the visual input. We are forced to conclude that signals representing experience converge with and modify the input to the visual input systems.[33]

A central issue is, *how* this ongoing matrix of intentionality is relating to the stresses it receives from reality.

EXPECTANCY TO HABITUATION

We observe that all biological systems exhibit a stability.[34] They are adapted to the environment in which the system has been operating. That is to say, they maintain a certain regularity of relationships to attain certain results. These are plans of behavior[35] from which actions are taken so far as there are tests in every piece of action which registers those differences which make a difference to the outcome of the plan. When these distinctions, or contrasts, are registered in the feature detectors or in other processing functions, then other alternate plans may be called into action, again, so as to maintain the organizational stability of the system.

Feed-forward mechanisms adjust the receptors to the level of sensitivity which the central organization or plan "arranges" as appropriate. The level of reception has something to do with the amount of "difference" which the system is ready to process. Small distinctions will not be worthy of attention whereas excess stress will be considered dangerous. For example, gamma efferent fibers which leave the center of the system with impulses to the kinesthetic receptors in the muscles determine just how sensitive the pressure receptors are. In the retina, similar impulses are sent to adjust visual capacity. This is a feed-forward process which organizes the behavior of the organism on the basis of its central plans.

There are central plans at higher levels which determine goals and directions and guide "decisions" made. Bernstein,[36] a neurophysiologist, writes:

> Whatever forms of the motor activity of higher organisms we consider, from elementary movements to multiphasic industrial processes, writing, articulation, analysis suggests no other guiding constant than the form and sense of the motor problem and the dominance of the required result of its solutions, which determine, from step to step, now the fixation and now the reconstruction of the course of the program as well as the realization of the sensory corrections.

In general, the data indicates that the biological organism tends to form sets of behavior and to become fixed in its repetitive actions. At the very lowest level of the nervous system, for example, we can observe a form of processing in which monotonous stimulation leads to a *decrease* of activity and the movement toward what is called *habituation*. In habituation, the system is being responsive by actively, if mechanically, integrating the process of its current interaction. It is programmed to act in this way for this time.

In perception of a global nature, Bruner has pointed out that we are always involved in acts of categorization which are forms of habituation. We expect certain things to happen, certain noises to come, certain pictures on the walls, etc. Bruner, Postman, and Rodriguez[37] used ordinary playing cards to demonstrate the facts of this kind of habituation of perception. Our past experience with playing cards evokes categories in which we are supposed to see red hearts and diamonds and black clubs and black spades. When the subjects of the experiment were shown a red ace of spades or a black eight of diamonds, they most often did not see the anomaly and unconsciously *corrected* the image. Again, we tend to see what we are habituated to see. Helmholtz called this "unconscious inference".

One component of nervous system behavior, then, is the active process of organizing. Another is search and sampling, to see what fits with expectancy.[38] Taken together, these two components raise the important question as to how change can occur in a system in which experience has already determined input and where habituation patterns are in force. It might appear that nothing new or unusual could enter such a system. Only what fits the given set of perceptual apparatus should be perceived. According to this thesis, one learns certain ways to see and then is fixed by these patterns for the rest of his life. Of course, much of human habit formation with its continual repetition of behavior-forms testifies to the prevalence of exactly this kind of behavior. And we know that some people are quite open to new experiences while others are all but completely shut off from them.

Sokolov[39] has pointed out that we apprehend reality in sets and that with only minor changes in a visual or auditory situation, we give no response. These sets are broken and the individual becomes aroused, "aware" when habituated orientation is changed along any of its given parameters. If there has been noise, silence creates alertness; if silence, noise will do the trick. In other words, once a form is created, the individual continues in that direction and orients his relationship to reality in accordance with his set until that set is broken.

The breaking of a set is subjectively experienced as emotion which begins when there is a non-fit perception.[40] The so-called "amount" of emotion describes, therefore, not an energetic quantitative difference, but the distinction in the fit with the expectancies; in other words, the amount of asymmetry the organism is involved in the third aspect of behavior, namely, what to do about the novelty. On a global level, there is perhaps an analogy to this in Thomas Kuhn's[41] carefully documented description of how theories determine the questions asked by scientists, govern the rules of their research, and fix the kinds of instruments they will use. According to Kuhn, it is only when a piece of data appears which does not fit the accepted paradigm that a change occurs. The theory and activity of science then shifts to the new direction now determined by whatever theory comes to organize these new data. That is, novelty activates research.

Thus, arousal is the result of non-fit, a sudden openness to an uncertainty. The non-fit makes it necessary for a searching for new patterning to begin—if the novelty is to be organized. Arousal is the felt emotion and its "quantity" is determined by the degree of non-fit.

ANXIETY

In Mandler's experiments,[42] animals and humans were subjected to situations in which they did not have a plan of behavior readily available for meeting an uncertainty, or an unexpected change. The experiments showed that both animals and humans become disorganized and the humans either become anxious or develop obsessive thoughts which, as Mandler points out, is actually a searching for a plan. In Schachter's work[43] subjects were given injections of adrenalin. This created a state of sympathetic activation, but no explanation was given to the subjects for their changed physical status. Schachter found that though the intensity of the emotional activation could be varied with the drug, the particular emotion varied on the basis of the labels the subject was given or used to explain his condition. The activated person could feel elated or depressed depending on the meaning he was given for the arousal. Anxiety appeared when no plan, that is, no labels, were given. Looked at another way, then, uncertainty produces anxiety and the need for a plan, wherein patterns of expectation and eventually habituation and closure are evolved.

OPENNESS AND CLOSURE

The Japanese neuropsychiatrists Kasamatsu and Hirai[44] studied the habituation of the orienting response to a repeating click in ordinary people and in Zen Masters. The subjects were put in a sound proof room and exposed to the click which was repeated every fifteen seconds. Normal subjects showed the expected response. There was a decrease in the response as measured by EEG after the third or fourth click. Apparently there was habituation. However, when the Zen Masters were exposed to this same repetitive click over a period of five minutes, they did not show habituation, but responded to the last click in the same way they had every other. In other words, they were able to *stay open* to the forming process and to the action-of-being-there in the world.

This experiment raises certain central questions and speculations. Perhaps as an organism is more and more open to wider area of novelty, it can develop the capacity to remain in openness. This would be a form which always is able-to-be an open process and to be aware of the most subtle shifts. This experiment may also point out that the process of habituation, to which we are all more or less subject, is a form itself. It is a form in which forming becomes closure and the more open responsivity to stimuli is discontinued; the novelty ceases to be new.

In the following chapters, we will be exploring this question. Forms of habituation are obviously necessary in some instances but central is the issue as to whether habituation is a necessary feature of biology, or whether, as the Zen Masters' response would seem to indicate, that openness is truly possible.

CHAPTER 3

Rigid Form and Form Against Form

Many psychoanalysts have written about the organization of personality into specific and more or less fixed forms. Kurt Goldstein[1] has noted the schizophrenic avoidance of the abstract and preference for the concrete. He found this is a definite patterning of behavior such that when abstract thinking is necessary, the schizophrenic exhibits definite evidence of anxiety. He also studied organically brain damaged patients and observed that they experience catastrophic anxiety when dislodged from the simplistic, concrete, rigid forms of behavior they have developed to arrange their world. In schizoid conditions, there may be a rigid form of self-enclosed concern, excluding the world.

In neurotics, as Karen Horney[2] has pointed out, the child who is raised in an environment which is inimical to his interests develops a feeling of being alone and isolated in a hostile world. Kelman[3] has emphasized that such a child has the feeling that no one is there for him, no one cares for him, and no one is on his side. The child's life is a constant experience of uncertainty. He cannot develop a consistent framework of operation because the environment in which he is living is fraught with ambiguity, and the implicit message is that there is something wrong with him. When he searches for clues as to how to live in a more harmonious way with the people around him, he discovers that he must abandon his own responses and pay attention to the responses demanded of him by the adult figures in his orbit. They, in their egocentricity and fear, require him to fit their patterns and needs and forget his own. Thus, whenever he meets with uncertainty, he cannot use his own integrating, curing capacity, and must find a mode *outside himself* to handle uncertainty. Eventually, this search for an external plan is realized by balancing the power he discovers in the demands that his family makes on him. By doing this, he is more and more unable to form and use his own experience to organize events which are uncertain. His forming processes become more and more rigidly structured and evolve into a general plan of behavior which Horney delineated as the *Pride System*. This plan a neurotic will use to guide his entire life.

As mentioned,* George Mandler[4] has shown that anxiety occurs when there is an interruption of behavior and there is no other available means of organization. When other forms of organization are easily and readily available, there is no anxiety. Mandler first demonstrated this with rats; he showed that if

*Chapter 2.

they were interrupted when hungry in the behavior of running a maze, they did not become hyperactive or develop convulsions. Reason: they could still fall into a *pattern* of food searching. If, on the other hand, they were satiated, they did not find this food searching plan of behavior in their repertoire and became quite quickly hyperexcited. In human studies, Mandler and others[5] have shown that "relevant" interruptions of behavior cause much less anxiety than do "irrelevant" interruptions, which leave the subjects without a plan. In other human studies, Mandler has shown that after interruption, a subject begins to have obsessive thoughts. This is apparently the subject's attempt to organize the interrupted sequence. He writes:

> It might be suggested that high anxiety subjects suffer more from the effect of interruption. Their arousal might have been greater since the success sequence was more highly organized. They respond to interruption first with the production of ruminative, obsessive thoughts and second with persistence rather than with choice of the less threatening task.

RIGID FORM: THE NEUROTIC PRIDE SYSTEM

Horney argues that the rigid plan of behavior she calls the "Pride System" is developed to achieve an outcome which the person has found insures his survival. The Pride System is, therefore, a plan of behavior which organizes anxiety. Any interruption of it will result in anxiety and the burst of efforts to restore the lost position. The basic feature of the Pride System is that the person organizes around an Idealized Image of himself. This is his cognitive/imaginative attempt to achieve an anxiety-free existence.

A child growing up in a disturbed family attempts to integrate his evolving needs with the family. For example, if power and safety can be obtained by his being compliant in his family, his plan will provide for actions which move to compliant behavior. He needs to be safe; safety is found through compliance and he must always act that nice way. His behavior becomes compulsive because he is unable to be with his own sense of uncertainty in the ongoing events of his life. He is driven to be nice, and he is desperate, and insatiable because he feels he has no other way of dealing with uncertainty. He experiences his plan as a *necessity* because interruption of it is so frightening. At this level of organization, the various circles of cognitive processing lead him to the feeling that his behavior (plan) is the only one for him. His form is that he feels he must be all giving or all loving, or he must be a saint in whatever arena he is operating. Within the basic plan, he finds patterns of behavior which further mold him into the plan and he begins to integrate around the image he "wants" to be. The direction of this behavior does not come from an inner center. It is *not important* what he likes or feels, but only how can he best serve the overall plan. At the next stage, the individual comes to feel he *is* his *Idealized Image* (the plan). He acts as if it were fact and he is the nicest, kindest person in the world.

The plan to achieve the perfect organization of behavior in the form of an idealized identity has subsidiary results. First, any input into the system (for example, his hostility) which does not fit the idealized concepts is not evaluated for what it is, but is processed on the basis of its fit into the system of pride. Such a person is, in effect, always trying to bring the self back into balance through trying to force himself back into the form of the Idealized Image. For example, Joe R. has said something to his boss which does not fit with Joe's Idealized Image of himself as the smartest and most perfect worker around. Joe does not evaluate what he said, what he was feeling, or how it evolved that he said it. He tells himself, "I should *not* have said it." He is not aware that he is avoiding engaging the unique fact of what actually happened and he does not see that he is primarily responding to his discovery that he is not being his Ideal.

Resignation, expansiveness, or self-effacement are interpersonal and intrapsychic forms of avoiding the uncertainty of the moment. When the environment does not act to fit the image—that is, when other people's actions do not confirm the individual's idea of himself—he may develop what Horney calls *claims*. These are demands that events should be the way he needs them to be. Because he needs to be liked by everyone, he feels he should be invited to every party he hears about. He expects the world to carry out this plan. He is a structural organization, which subjectively experiences himself as the sort of person who is invited to parties; when reality does not confirm this form, it creates an interruption in his plan and anxiety supervenes. The behavior which results is a process of feeling he *should* have been invited; he is insulted and humiliated. He does not take note of the conditions that might have caused his not being invited. He simply feels the fact as not fitting his system.

The process of self-hate which follows the failure of the realization of the ideal can be appreciated as being a part of the overall plan. Analysts often hear patients stress how terrible they are or how bad they are if they have feelings which they think are bad, or if they do something they feel to be less than beautiful. Despite all assurances to the contrary, the torrents of self-disgust, self-contempt, and self-hate may flow with unmitigated strength. Some patients even find a kind of nobility in their immolation which is transformed into a feeling that they are abused by the world. We can see that this is really a continuation of the avoidance of seeing reality. As a state of organizing, it assumes the person is something other than what he is. To reveal to himself the discrepancy between the facts and the assumptions would lead him into the actual consideration of the uncertainty of his experiential process. This is forbidden by the basic organization of the system because it would call for a struggle with the ambivalence and anxiety that is the actuality of his present.

Horney notes that the goal of the pride system is to raise the person over others. This is the interpersonal mode for achieving the goals of the basic plan: to prevent the unfolding of uncertainty or disorganization. Before one can accept another in his own right, he must have some recognition of his own separateness. A person besieged by his own sense of inadequacy cannot acknowledge his separateness. To recognize separate persons would be to open up the issue of the similarities and the differences between people. Separateness establishes polarities and novelties and demands openness. It means opening up to the organizing and shifting of feelings and an engagement in the task of constantly recategorizing: that changing forming we call human relating. It can raise the ghosts of old memories, of tensions that have occurred in the past with other "separate" people such as the mother, the memory of many small moments of pain. It can lead to the larval feeling of wonder about one's position with another. The pride system is designed to prevent such confrontations. It relates from image to image, making sure that the self-image maintains its status of being "better than the other". This status makes it unnecessary to engage any other as equal or to flow with experience in the here and now. The interpersonal behavior of someone under the aegis of the pride system is primarily reactive and is based on the use of other people as a means to the end of assuring safety from any and all uncertainty.

Basically, then, a neurotic feels he does not have the capacity for the present challenge. He is unable to allow a shift in the relationship of the abstract (his conceptualization of the experience) and the concrete (the experience itself). Normally, when there is a playing with the relationship between the abstract (conceptualization) and the concrete (the primary experience), the entire personality is called into action. Normally, when the form of the whole (the abstract) shifts, there are new relationships to other parts (the concrete) of the organism and to the world. This opens up the possibility of further change. It may lead to new kinds of connections to other people and to real interests. But for the neurotic, this process is a cause for immense anxiety.[6,7]

Mrs. O. would immediately experience anxiety and eventually psychosomatic symptoms if she became interested in anything. One day, hearing a radio program about white mice, she immediately began to think about what her interests would mean. She fantasized that they might lead her to take courses in college. She might even become interested in other animals and in doing biological research. If that happened, she was sure her interests would be so absorbing that she would end up going for a Ph.D. and then would not have time to be married and live with a man who would take care of her. She would be on her own, an autonomous person. The initial interest in white mice had opened up new kinds of relationships and Mrs. O. fell prey to anxiety. Eventually she blocked the whole process out by retreating to her room and masturbating, one of her usual modes of integrating situations of stressful proportions.

CHANGE IN THE RIGID SYSTEM

In analysis, the rigid system can be broken down in analytic sessions and a patient can suddenly open up to various experiencing, allowing himself to go through the anxiety while trying to find out what generalizations can be made about the new experience. A woman, for example, believes that everyone with right wing views is bad. As she talks to me in a session, she realizes someone she met the day before has these views, but that she has very warm feelings toward him. There is confusion and anxiety, but gradually she is able to see that there are other feelings and other ways to order her being with people. In this, she is loosening up some of her feelings about herself and is allowing herself to be open to feelings. This represents a change in her ordering process.

FORM AGAINST FORM: SCHIZOPHRENIA

For the schizophrenic, the dilemma of experience is more seriously confused than for the neurotic. Patients who mould into the schizophrenic form came to feel, early in life, that they could not connect the abstract and the concrete. Their "experience" is, consequently, always a combination of pain and obfuscation. They are blocked from participation in the forming process by the nature of their family system, for whenever they attempt to bring the abstract and the concrete together, it is taken as a threat to this system and hence to their own security. Haley[8] quotes the following interchange:

Patient: Oh, all right, but it–it wasn't that exactly. No, I am not giving ground–uh–it's hard to explain this thing. Uh-uh-what was I going to say. (short pause) I mean I felt that this–this is what I mean, uh–that I felt that you could have been a better mother to me than you were. So there were things . . .

Mother: Uh–

Father: Well you said . . .

Patient: (interrupting) You could have been better than you were. So that's why–that's that–I felt–it was, uh, uh, was all right to . . .

Mother: Well, if you meant it that way, that's perf–that's what I wanted to know–and that's all I care–you see. But I will say, Simon, that if you would take your father and mother just like they're plain people–you just come here and went through life like anybody else went through life like anybody else went through–and–and don't keep in picking on them and picking them to pieces–but just leave them alone–go along with them the way they are–and don't change them–you'll be able to get along with everybody. I assure you.

The patient has difficulty in remembering as soon as he enters the concrete and he starts to question the sanctity of the mother's abstraction. He is about to say how he feels, but this violates the system's rule that the mother's needs must dominate. The mother's response keeps the boy from challenging her view of reality. She exhorts him to be "like everybody else" and to treat his parents as plain people. There are numerous embedded assumptions in this statement which are important to clarify.

First, one aspect of her thinking is the idea that there is a "way to go through life"; that one way is right. Implicit in this is that this one way involves accepting the parents as they are in their "way" of going through life. Lidz[9] has noted that it is the needs of the parents which dominate reality in schizophrenic families. These parents speak of "a way". Of course, to believe there is only one way to go obliterates the process of forming and denies the ambiguity and paradox of existence. It organizes the shades and distinctions into rigid forms.

Secondly, the mother's exclamation is an order to the patient to blend himself out of the picture by leaving his parents alone. It is a central fact that all human personality is a result of identification with parents and others (teachers and friends). The mother suggests that the boy leave her alone, which is obviously impossible as long as he is alive. (This is the double bind we will discuss below.) In this statement, the mother creates a pseudo-conflict-free and question-free environment. She seems anxious to block any question about her perfection and to clear away any possibility that there might be feelings and doubt about what happens. In one family situation I observed, I heard the following interchange:

Patient: I'm thirsty, I think I will get a drink of water.
Mother: What's wrong, can't you wait until the session is over?

The depth and continual questioning of a patient's minutest participation in the concrete is seen in the immediate challenge to the ample spontaneous sense of thirst.

Thirdly, and most central to this process, is the implication that what the child feels is not relevant. He is considered by the family system to be an infinitely malleable substance which can be made to fit the mold of the family demands. There is a distinct denial of anything the individual might feel himself; for the family to acknowledge his feeling would be to create another pole. Polarity demands relating. It is forbidden.

Haley has pointed out that schizophrenic families have certain rules of communication. The major ones prescribe that not only is no statement ever affirmed but there is also consistent disqualifying of whatever is said. The family relationships are compulsory, often taking the form of a pseudo-mutuality. The effective overall spirit of these family rules is that there is no support for any member of the family to express an autonomous position. Constantly undercutting the personal statements of children is a confirmed technique for decreasing their sense of self-worth. We have seen it employed in brain washing techniques.

Haley's points coincide with, and are extended by, the recent work of Singer and Wynne.[10] The latter have demonstrated that communication in schizophrenic families is especially disturbed at attentional levels, whereas in the families in other psychiatric entities, it is disturbed at later periods, after attentional focus has developed.

Singer and Wynne express a concept of "shared foci of attention" which has four sequentially related processes. First, one person selects an event, feeling or perception for attention. He then makes an effort to orient the other person to that set; that is, he moves to tell the other to see it, hear it, or feel it, but in every way interacts and encourages the other to share an experience. In that effort, a sustained transaction occurs and there is a closure around meaning. In their family studies of the schizophrenic, Singer and Wynne have demonstrated that parents of schizophrenics talk in ways that leave a listener without a sense of encountering closure; there is an impression of being diverted, shunted about, and attention shifting. Meaning is impaired by a tendency to use words peculiarly, deviant reasoning and odd expressions. Statistically, there is so much of this piecemeal blurred thinking, talking and communicating, that it is difficult to visualize or comprehend the point of any discussion.

In normal development, parental interaction with children involves constantly helping a child to focus on particularities of the environment and helping him to understand and organize the perceptions which flow into his system. In other words, to help a child merge subject and object, abstract and concrete. In this way a child's perception processes are confirmed and given direct support.

As we will see later,* the progress of personality reorganization must flow through a stage of focusing similar to this if patients who have been prevented in early childhood from acquiring these focusing skills are ever to find themselves. In addition to the encouragements of overt processes, there are also numerous moments when a silent look of love and affirmation by the parent communicates a total acceptance of a child's being. In this, there is a confirmation for the younger member to move into the world and explore the use of his being, as well as a confirmation of the parent's position. In families where attentional support is lost, the child's experiences are disqualified. As a result, the normal organization of perceptual sets from experiencing cannot occur. There is, instead, pseudo-experiencing, based on the acceptance of parental plans, rather than the evolution of plans out of exercising function.

Bateson, Jackson, Haley and Weakland[11] have outlined the "double-bind" as characteristic in schizophrenic families. In this we see the following:

1. When the individual is involved in an intense relationship; that is, a relationship in which he feels it is vitally important that he discriminate accurately what sort of message is being communicated so that he may respond appropriately.
2. And, the individual is caught in a situation in which the other person in the relationship is expressing two orders of message and one of these denies the other.
3. And, the individual is unable to comment on the messages being expressed to correct his discrimination of that order of message to respond to, i.e., he cannot make a meta-communicative statement.

The dilemma of an individual in a double-bind is profound; it is a difficulty which must be seen as a function of the rules of the overall situation. The first rule is that he is in an intense relationship: he is in "the soup". But that is only

*Chapter 12.

part of it, for this relationship has a certain quality. The schizophrenic needs his parents desperately and needs his relationship with his family to continue just as the family needs for him to continue to be in the double-bind. The only available response for the schizophrenic is to be not autonomous. That is, to be unaware of the connection between the abstract and the concrete, subject and object. The family system blocks the process of confronting novelty. Further, when a schizophrenic is faced with a double message, he is not permitted the meta position. That would entail observation of the dialectics of double messages. Through seeing conflict, duplicity, and paradox, and through confronting them, he would catapult the whole family into the very anxiety they fear. Such a situation would create an unacceptable dissolution of the symbiotic self-abnegation which is necessary for the survival of the family group. As a result of his intolerable bind, the patient frequently goes into a "psychotic" or unreal response. Such behavior blurs the issue, but it has an advantage: it avoids the anxiety of autonomy. It is a compulsive move to absolve oneself from the possibility of participation in experience.

Laing says[12]:

> In over a hundred cases where we have studied the actual circumstances around the social event when some person comes to be regarded as a schizophrenic, it seems to us that *without exception* the experience and behavior that gets labelled schizophrenic is a *special strategy that a person invents in order to live in an unliveable situation.* In his life situation a person has come to feel he is in an untenable position. He cannot make a move, or make no move without being beset by contradictory and paradoxical pressures and demands, pushes and pulls, both internally from himself, and externally, from those around him. He is, as it were, in a position of checkmate.

Family studies of schizophrenia demonstrate how the parents of schizophrenics encourage their children to deny their individuality. The schizophrenic family is a group with the global undifferentiated identity of a unit; no one member exists in his or her own right; he or she is only because "the family is" and he "must never" stand out as a separate entity. Time and again in these families, it is observed that whenever anyone expresses a feeling, as did the patient who was thirsty, he is undercut by some other member.

The patients we call schizophrenic evolve a form of being, or set, which is descriptively detachment. This detachment is, in effect, a deep commitment (in form) to the refusal to engage in forming. The schizophrenic's experience of the process of unifying the abstract and the concrete has been tinged by pain. As a result, he has developed a deep suspicion of all forming and all form. Frequently, there is an extreme sensitivity to the minutest signs of coercion, in part because of the schizophrenic's suspicion of anything that would lead him into consolidating in one shape. His commitment to the absence of forming is accomplished by avoiding any awareness of his form in formlessness. In sum, the ongoing awareness of a schizophrenic follows the logic of avoiding any process that leads into being organized.

Rose G., at the beginning of her analytic work, could not stand to have me look at her. She felt my looking gave her some shape. She was afraid I might get hooked into the wrong idea about her and then I could never get out of that. If I saw her looking at anything, that was bad because she was caught in a position and felt hemmed in. She wanted to watch me, without my knowledge. She was watching me to see how I was before she began relying on me in a relationship. We spent several analytic sessions in which we both kept our eyes closed. She did not want to engage in the openness of relating before being sure she had a form which she could trust. If I commented that she was different from one day to the next, she would become intensely annoyed. I had designated her as one form before, and now as something different. I had acknowledged implicitly, thereby, that she was forming and form. This was intolerable.

Unfortunately for the schizophrenic, whatever set he may evolve, the process of living stubbornly refuses to acknowledge it and continues to offer novelty. The change of the body, the aging process, and the new developmental tasks which continue until death, are continual novelties which demand integration. Schizophrenic and neurotic forms are sets organized to avoid the engagement with novelty, but the possibility for novelty is always there and each time it is encountered there is activation and exercise of capacities of the system.

AVOIDING NOVELTY

The person who avoids novelty operates as if he were incapable of organizing new data. We know that people who act in this way feel weak and unsure of themselves. When any input or output is "recognized" as not fitting their structures, they feel that they cannot handle it. In such a system, the person may integrate in closing-off forms as did Mrs. O. when she masturbated to avoid her interest in white mice. Since life is continually changing and open, this means that the system is in danger at all times.

Sets which avoid novelty are, in fact, implicitly attempts to remain out of the experience of awkwardness. Uncertainty leads into awkwardness and opens up feelings of impotence and weakness.* The experience of impotence and vulnerability is one which everyone would like to avoid. The avoidance is so basic that it is rarely mentioned by patients in psychoanalysis. Patients will speak instead of the omnipotence they fear and want, and may describe the impotence they feel when they are not omnipotent, but they do not speak of the impotence and uncertainty they experience in attempts to master novelty. To escape this impotence they may try to bury themselves in life's events and in the pseudo-mutuality of superficial relationships. They may marry and raise children, go to work and live out their lives but they undergo a moment by moment pressure to avoid this feeling of uncertainty and weakness.

A man will sit down to read a book; fifteen minutes later he will jump up to

*See Chapter 6.

paint the garage, feeling he has to do the paint job; it needs "doing" he says; he is only vaguely conscious of the process he is in during those crucial fifteen minutes. During that time, in a gradually rising crescendo, he is getting interested in the book. He is having associations and connections to many different experiences which the book recalls. These connections are disparate and disorganized so they lead him to anxiety. He is into uncertainty. As a result, he feels it is necessary to move to behavior which he can more easily organize, thereby avoiding the novelties he encountered in his interest in the book. On further investigation, we may discover this man sees himself as a weak, emaciated, and poverty-stricken soul. He cannot conceive of himself as having any capacities to actualize his interests.

Similarly, a woman says she feels she does not "have a foothold on life". She feels like a film, she has experiences, but they go through her; there is no reaction to involvement. She says, "You would not expect a film to do anything, but record and that is all I feel I do."

AROUSAL, NOVELTY, ENGAGEMENT

A new mode of behavior is *possible* when the organism is aroused. "The clarifying articulation of any forming process is an active novel moment. By fiat, seeing is a challenge and an experience. Searching and scanning occurs and a person begins to see a new mode of handling events in other ways. It begins his change of processing procedures."[13]

In arousal, it is not so much that the individual changes his old forms, but more accurately, is forced to see the factual acting-being he is in this human-relating process. Through practice and *participation in experience*, he comes to know how he is living, his ways of dealing with that living, and the possibilities that these ways of dealing offer. His novelty is that he sees how he is and how he is different. This opens up questions for him to consider.

A mere shift in behavior control or a shift in beliefs is not necessarily real change. That may mean the person has simply exchanged one set of ideas or concepts for another. But if a change is the result of this experience of engaging uncertainty and novelty, then the person has come through arousal and this experience offers the possibility for growth; it encourages him to try himself out in other new situations. There is a change in the individual's ongoing structure of behavior. Moreover, the practice and participation in engaging novelty lead to feedback, which indicates a completion or realization of an act. This positive feedback encourages a deeper faith in engaging novelty whenever it appears.

A confrontation of issues with an exploration of a new set means integration. Secondarily the organism individuates. Often this looks like a matter of teleology as there is development of capacities. In fact, the unfolding is only apparent purpose, or teleotomy, and development follows confrontation.[14] Psychoanalysts see over and over in sessions that patients feel more open and alive when they are "able" to confront, engage, experience, and move *through* problems and paradoxes instead of around them. When they *commit* themselves to working on uncertainties instead of avoiding them, they feel more new capacities becoming available. Just as the exercising of physical function can result in a muscle which is a muscle at its best, the exercise of engagement can result in a personality which is tough morally, knowing integrally what it wants and how it can meet the needs of its situation.

* * *

From here on in this book, we will be considering the process I call self-articulation, which is the experience of confronting novelty, leading to and emerging out of the disintegration of old forms. In general, we will approach this by looking at the kinds of negative modes of forming we have seen here, the miscreations, forms such as those found in the mental diseases we call neurosis and schizophrenia. These are forms of closure which prevent the development of autonomous function. As we will observe, with the breakdown of these personality forms as the result of environment and/or psychoanalytic influences, there arises opportunity for self-creation, through the exercise of forming capacities.

Part II

THE CREATIVE THRUST

CHAPTER 4

Incipient Processes

Any major shift in personality can only occur in stages. And the first stage is that of *incipient events*, in which there is a breakthrough *of* a new form of behavior. A total breakthrough *to* the behavior might not come for years. For the moment, the incipient events simply create possibility for new, more total organizations. They suggest to the person who has heretofore "thought" himself to be fixed, that it is possible for him to engage in new behavior.

The therapist's fundamental responsibility at this early stage is to alert his patient to the new facts of forming, and to help him become aware of the possibilities that have now presented themselves for further evolution. The analyst's care is important as he notes that every new form is a mode of integrating growing-edge issues. When the incipient event occurs, the analyst should make clear that it is an indication the patient's capacity to integrate is becoming available.

CONTRAST MAY STIMULATE THE INCIPIENT EVENT

The number of ways in which the incipient event can be stimulated is virtually infinite. For example, one may read a book or a poem about someone who did something for himself. This may stimulate the reader to remember times when he did the same. It may catch him at a moment when he can see the possibility for his own activities mobilized in an autonomous direction. Or the book may offer the reader a contrast to his own inertial and self-abnegating ways. He may then feel a distinction which will stimulate process organizing and will be the beginning of something new.

Max P. sees a television show in which two women are contrasted. One of the women is detached and hates everything and everyone around her. The other is interested and involved in her family and in her life. The two women are in a semi-private room in a hospital, both with serious illnesses. The woman who is more involved seems to my patient the more alive and capable individual. It is apparent that living through the illness is quite a different process for her than for the other who is absorbed by her self-pity and egocentricity. Max reports to me that this second woman seemed sad while being quite miserable to the nurses and that the first seemed more flexible and conveyed a joy of wisdom and strength. As he recognizes this difference between the two women, Max wonders about his own life. He knows he has been demanding, egocentric, and rigid and has avoided relating with his children and wife. He feels how tense and anxious his life is compared to that of the woman in the television program who moved with equanimity through the pain she was experiencing. Max feels her equanimity contrasts with his temper tantrums which occur whenever he is asked to be involved in family affairs. From a working through of this distinction, we can date the beginning of incipient events in which he became a process of feeling more into his home life. One weekend, shortly after our session about the show, Max's nine-year-old son had his birthday. For the first time in our five years of work together, Max spoke of his distinct warm feelings for his boy. But after the discussion began, he developed a violent headache and a tension in his entire body. The mobilization of new organization, one more directed to his connections with people, was manifested in this tension. He was breaking the old connections of his compulsive detachment and creating new ones. Old generalizations of what he considered to be the order of the world were rapidly being dissolved and new ones created.

When a therapist can point out how the patient is driven to be certain ways, it sometimes reduces the secret pride the patient takes in his behavior. The patient can see that the behavior is repetitive, and that the results of it are sterile. While realizing this about the way he is, he can begin to see his outlines and his connections with the world of objects and processes. He is then automatically catapulted into a process of contrasting his own facticity, now articulated, with the facticity of other positions which have come into focus. When the fixity of his present form becomes apparent, through a contrast, the patient may begin to remember ways he functioned differently in the past. These memories often convey a mode of being in which he was operating more in a connection to himself. These memories are often of sensory motor forms, activities in which the person was working with "raw material". In the memories, he is directly perceiving the world without an abstractive process.

Fred D., for example, had spent much of life involved in vindictive behavior. It was important for him to keep other people down and under him. He would manage this in both subtle and gross forms. He could not stand it if he was in any way in debt to others or if he was, in any way, vulnerable to them. As he began to appreciate all of these forms of his vindictiveness, he had a memory: on the way home from grammar school he had used to kick a piece of wood on the concrete pavement. He remembered the delicious, sensuous sound of the wood hitting the pavement. He remembered he would repeat it over and over with delight, without a care for anything else in the world. I felt a deep respect for this memory as I sensed he was beginning to resonate, with a kind of elegant simplicity, to his own authentic experience of aloneness and his efforts to master his personal reality. The memory was. of course, related to his need for triumph and vindictiveness (the goals of his pride system), but it was also a shade closer to the real well of loneliness that had generated this pride form. The sounds and the capacity to hear and enjoy them were in direct contrast to his rigid need for control and exposed him to an experience of uncertainty, novelty, and arousal.

Inputs from these contrasts start to accumulate and act as preparation so that further inputs can stimulate incipient processes; the old organization begins to shift. One patient said:

> Several times recently it has been brought to my attention I actually occupy space in somebody's mind. Although it is all mixed up with my role playing, it is also independent of my role playing. Occupying space is having an identity, role playing seeks to persuade somebody when nothing is there. At times, it may seem like an acceptable substitute for occupying space. If you do not have weight and occupy space it is necessary to have role playing—it is an obscure fact, but I haven't solved the problem yet of materialization, the matter of weight, occupying space; most remarkable. I took my friend, John (a three-year-old), out Sunday; this was a strong example of how much delight I can have in the space I occupy in his mind.

One woman begins to experience some incipient kinds of change when she runs into someone on the bus who remembers her from the year before at school. She is surprised that she is remembered and feels a sudden sense of existence in the fact that she has a place in someone's memory. She feels a thatness about herself and a thereness that has not existed before. In effect, this input confirms her presence. The other person's recognition of her organizes and acknowledges her processes as a unity: herself. She has lived in a cloud of feeling buffeted about by the events of her life. She has seemed to herself to have no organization and is astounded and delighted to find someone who appreciates her as having one.

Mrs. O. was always astonished if anyone called her by her first name; she would get a "chilly tingling" in her legs with the other's delight of recognition. Another woman would become shocked if someone commented on her looks. Such events capture these people as "one" and they feel, for a moment, that they are units of consequence. Many have not, until that point, even seen themselves as one body, though the material fact seems unavoidable.

SCHIZOPHRENIC PSYCHOSIS AS AN INCIPIENT EVENT

Incipient processes may be recognized in the appearance of information from the environment which contradicts the self-image. A person acts in some way which produces feedback that does not confirm his sense of disorganization. It comes back to him that he can be in a different form, one which is organized by himself. It is a taste of the possible which contradicts his negative self-image.

This is particularly clear in work with schizophrenic patients. As a type, schizophrenics are the most undeveloped people analysts see. As we have indicated, all data, both research and clinical, indicates that the early life of this group of individuals occurs in an environment which specializes in undercutting and destroying self-esteem,[1,2] the ability to form. In the moment by moment interaction between the parent and child there is constant disqualification and mystification of whatever is said. Relationships in these families exhibit a lack of feeling, are alienated and detached.[3,4] In this atmosphere, even minimal development of function does not occur. What develops, instead, is a form which is a caricature of function, a form which is unable to integrate novelty. Since schizophrenics cannot explore the uncertainty of their early developmental processes, the functioning in trial and error does not occur and they have only the form given to them by the family. As a result, they have been condemned to the use of rigid form.[5,6]

When faced with a disorganization of this form, the schizophrenic patient becomes intensely anxious. If he is unable to find some way to order this disorder, he may form a psychotic organization which is, in effect, the aberrant undeveloped functioning of the forming capacity.

Many psychotic episodes arise out of the schizophrenic's new and acute awareness of humanness.[7] This awareness is often a result of a close relationship with another human being. Immediately preceding many, if not most, psychoses, the individual has come to realize himself as a human among other humans. In an intense emotional relationship with a significant other, the schizophrenic experiences the existential fact that he has feelings and rights to express and realize himself. We often find that this significant other person has left the patient for some reason just prior to the onset of the psychotic process. This leaving has revealed to the patient his loneliness and accentuates the awareness of what he has just had and has now lost. It may be also that there was a kind of symbiosis which is suddenly broken and leaves the schizophrenic, now having begun to feel, suddenly on his own. Silverman[8] believes the psychotic process begins with a "subjective evaluation of oneself as being incapable of experiencing any effective control over a life situation".

Pious[9] observed that his patient seemed to begin a changing state whenever there was a withdrawal either in the therapeutic situation by the therapist (consciously or unconsciously) or by some significant other in the world. He noted that in the "withdrawal", the patient expressed a feeling of "emptying" which was followed by a "slipping" and then a "focusing" in which the patient said, "For the time it takes me to see things again these little details become my whole life." This is followed by a "perplexity, blinking, bizarre, apparently incoherent verbalizations and episodes of estrangement". This sequence of these responses indicates Pious is describing a patient who has moved into the first stage of organizing, and is faltering in uncertainty. He is feeling and aware of new possibilities. He sees things in detail and experiences anxiety about how to make sense of them. This is similar to the focal attention Schactel[10] has described for the artist and child.

Ornitz[11] reviewed the literature on perception in psychosis and concluded that sensory changes probably precede full blown psychosis. He shows that most reports of schizophrenic pre-psychotic perception demonstrate a "faulty modulation" or "breakdown of the homeostatic regulation of sensory input . . ."

The patients are hyposensitive to extreme stimuli and hypersensitive to weak stimuli. But fundamental to their state is a lack of adequate organization. Patient after patient describes being overwhelmed and unable to arrange his world.

Silverman calls this stage the stage of "preoccupation, isolation, estrangement". He writes, "During this period of intense personal preoccupation one tends to become absorbed in a narrow circle of ideas." He quotes Sullivan on the early throes of this state:

His [the patient's] awareness is now that of a twilight state between waiting and dreaming; his facial expression is that of absorption in ecstatic inner experiences, and his behavior is peculiar to the degree that he no longer eats or sleeps, or tends to any of the routines of life.

Every investigator of the psychotic process has emphasized that this initial period is marked by an involvement with self. This is acutely obvious to the observer and is vividly experienced by the subject. The patient has become present for himself as a live, ongoing perceiver of reality. He has been taught to be like everybody else, but now he drops the mask and moves into his own senses. One patient wrote of this experience (Jefferson[12]):

that I have missed all the main issues of life and can see nothing clearly. That I have concerned myself with externals only and have missed all the meanings of the great inner significance. That there is no such thing as a normal mind and an abnormal mind, but only minds and more minds. That life is the important thing and not the classification of it. Life to live it and not fear it. Let it rip. Let it be destructive if it must, but live it and do not fear it.

This is what Ellenberger[13] has called a "creative illness". The initial phase is characteristically an absorption with the self and with subjective feelings of utter isolation. Scher[14] considers the first stage of a schizophrenic process to be one of intending or intention, a movement toward a "self determining" expression. The individual becomes "a person of decision, someone to be dealt with as a true individual". To fulfill the commitment of intending, a person must be "continually in a process of becoming or coming into being . . ."

Often, quite angrily, the psychotic person has to see where he actually stands. He knows, with a suddenness, that he has been living according to inauthentic standards and he begins his search for authenticity. There is a kind of shattering honesty to these moments that has been felt by many who have worked with psychotic patients.

The awakening period in the psychosis is spoken of by Bowers[15] as "Destructuring of Perception and Affect". He has found "heightened awareness" and a feeling of urgency. Schizophrenics may feel that "their minds have awakened and that they are functioning at a high level or that their creative powers are enhanced".

In this moment, the schizophrenic begins to discover the fallacy: that his schizophrenic form is the only way to organize. Psychosis is an investigation of personal feelings. The psychotic says such things as, "I am not myself." He sees that he has neglected what he is and feels that painful lack of connection between what he is and what he has been. He knows his inauthenticity and with this he is thrust into being himself, into loneliness and aloneness. Memories, meanings, and perceptions begin to be in a flow. Bowers writes that ideas of reference make their appearance at this point and a psychotic feels a "press for meaning". This is another way of saying the process is moving the individual into seeing and needing to see the patterns of his own personal feelings—a new event for him.

Incipient organizations tend to emerge at first in flashes of appreciation. As these flashes accumulate, they may, for a moment, direct the entire organization. There is often a personal satisfaction and self-acceptance and for a brief period, a person is mobilized. An example of this can be seen in Tom, who discovers he likes reading Milton's "Paradise Lost".

One night, Tom stays up until morning outlining its themes, wondering about its meaning, and working out the structure the author had created. Tom's mood is quiet, his mind is working on the poem and is not distracted, as it usually is, by sexual fantasies. The next morning, however, he is back into his old practices, again unable to decide how he wants to spend his time. He is around the house feeling distracted and uninterested in his previous night's fascinations.

In the poetry of Milton, Tom discovers in himself, among other things, a willingness to move into the terrors and uncertainties of being alone in the world. This experience of discovery is also a finding of his way into his own anxiety about his place in the frightening world of his family. The experience breaks through his protective processes of needing to have everything rigidly controlled and acquaints him with the joys of working with the unknown. He finds, for a moment, that he is able to connect the uncertainties of the world to himself in a living present. Indeed, he feels, for that time, "alive".

Similarly, Patient B talks for thirty-five minutes in a session about the way he obstructs his connections with his interests and his feeling. He says he has met a girl at school the day before and she gave him a big smile. He knows she smiles this way at everybody, but he liked the smile and felt good when he received it. B then begins to weave his ideas of what the smile meant, how much she likes him, etc. He comments he does this with everything. He constantly weaves ideas and concepts in his head about the meanings of events. This leads him to recall his childhood preoccupation with a secret garden where he was in control. He knew every niche and corner of this fantasy world and had lived in it for many years. After listening to this for a half hour, I say: "So you obstruct your connection with your *now*." B jumps up from the couch and says my statement has resulted in an electrical impulse shooting down his spine. He is flushed all over and his eyes are vibrant. Whereas he had been talking in a monotone saying he felt sick with a cold, his talk is now lively and dynamic. He says he is suddenly aware of my presence and feels himself submitting to his feeling about me and what I said. He goes on, more openly now, to express feeling serious about going to medical school. He says he has always believed himself inadequate as a man and felt he only existed as a Brain. He believed his ability to use his hands was inadequate. When working in zoology lab, he saw however, he was no worse than others in being able to manipulate the experimental animals and the instruments. B is beginning now to feel he might learn to use his hands. I sense his connection with the outside world, my presence in this case, had opened him to this processing activity. He was in a state of arousal and began to associate to his hands. His hands are symbolic of his forming, integrating processes which are beginning to function and bring him together as a unit in his own right. B begins in the incipient event to make connections to the outside world heretofore unavailable from his narcissistic position. He recognizes me as separate as he begins to integrate the novelty of my presence in my words. As a result, he becomes a presence himself. He recognizes his "denial of the now" when my words and presence create a "now" which is a novelty for his shape of self-enclosed repetition. B also begins to remember the hand activity of his partners in the lab. That perception helps establish the boundaries of the others to which he can relate. The activity of his integration, general and specific, creates the boundaries of self-in-action. These are, as yet, tenuous because of the weakness or lack of binding in the initial stages. The connection of the subsystem–his hands–with other subfunctions of his organisms is not at all firmly established. The organizing of novelty needs a generalizing connection with multiple aspects of experience which has not yet occurred. His "hand" ability is minimally developed because he has had only minimal integrating experience with it. This function must be "connected" to the whole through specific acts–will build up a structure through action. This will provide for coding of subsequent novel events. The appearance of too much disorganized eventing will probably lead to a shift back to old forms. But in any case, the new form now makes possible many new and novel experiences heretofore not perceived from the narcissistic position. Most of the behavior will continue in the old forms but new perceptions will be possible. When new perceptions appear, they will create disturbances, questions about ways to understand, and anxiety, as with Tom, who was aroused by "Paradise Lost" and then after his involvement retreated the next day to his old forms.

It can be said that the person who learns something new about himself, for instance that he can use his hands, begins to accumulate more new facts about himself because the old facts now look different. Patient B saw he could use his hands and his feeling about his whole body began to change as he *saw* it with these hands. He began to realize that his old view of himself as incompetent did not fit with the new ideas about his hands. Consequently, he began to give more consideration to the different and unexpected aspects of himself. For the first time, now at age thirty-five, he began to talk to people. He began, while in therapy, to have a few passing relationships and then a few intimate, non-sexual, types of contact. He came to realize he did not want to spend his life in the research laboratory and tentatively applied to medical school. He took some of the courses he needed for admission. The experience in the zoology laboratory had led to a sense of his capacities and a shift in his view of himself. He realized he had a body and activity functions in which he could develop as a self.

BLOCKS TO INCIPIENT PROCESSES

Quite often, however, the patient experiences the incipient processes as dangerous and the facts which accumulate to establish a new form are challenged. This is because whatever input comes to the nervous system comes against sets of organization which have predisposed the system in specific and more or less fixed directions. Analysts often see patients who have come to believe they are worthless. These patients will violently oppose any evidence (or input) to the effect that they are, in fact, able to perform capably or that their lives have meaning. If it is pointed out to such a patient that he has done something which has significance beyond the mere performance, there is an oppositional reaction.

One of my patients, John, had for years been afraid of his movement in the direction of "homosexuality". Among other things, "homosexuality" meant to him the soft and warm concerned feelings he had but had never allowed to emerge. Eventually, he began to allow these feelings to come forth in the form of an affair with a younger man. The details of John's progress to this point will be discussed later,* but suffice it to say here that at this juncture, John became deeply involved with a beautiful, dark-complexioned twenty-five year old boy and told me endlessly how important it was for him that this very dependent and passive young man become independent. John was himself a driving, ambitious, middle-aged executive who had never acknowledged his own dependency. He felt terrible anxiety whenever his lover would go out in the street looking for another man. John knew that inevitably the boy would choose to be "fucked by a big, strong man". John found it terrible that this young boy would be "fucked over by an older man who'd use him for momentary relief". As I hear this, I recalled that one of John's primary screen memories was of his father sadistically marching him up and down in the alleyway next to their home. John was carrying a baton; the father, in front of the neighbors, was yelling laughingly, "now march", obviously using his son to show off and gratify his own power. John did not realize, or had blocked out recognition of his father's cruelty, but as he told me of his need to save this young man, I was aware that for the first time, he was speaking up for himself. I stressed this as I worked with him, indicating I felt that he was beginning, in this form, to reach out to help himself. I focused on the novel inner dimension: he had lived in

---

*Chapter 14.

sadistic fantasy, self-hate, and masochistic cruelty to himself, but now, his concern for the young man was a way of confronting this pain.

When a therapist highlights the fact that a new behavior is an experience in forming, a patient may react in several ways. He may block and refuse to recognize the presence of the new events. This is because the possibility creates considerable anxiety. John was often incredibly anxious to the point of needing tranquilizers. On one occasion, about a year before the homosexual affair, John told me he was having a recurrent dream that a little black boy was chasing him. This little boy was quite angry and in the dream John was running away from him. I gently asked what would happen if he turned and faced this boy. John became quite pale and silent. After a few minutes in which we were together in quiet, he told me he was feeling dizzy and nauseated. He then began to talk about a different topic. We later learned that the black boy symbolized an aspect of John he was afraid to accept. John did not feel he could live with himself if the little black boy was the decider and main guide of his self. I, perhaps a bit too hastily, attempted to urge him into the fray and he paled at the thought. At that time he needed to reduce the tension created by independence. One year later, he began to support an independence process in the externalized form of his young love. In supporting his friend, he was engaging the inarticulate, dispersed forming of himself. He was facing the black boy at a distance. I remarked to John, "I think you are beginning to object to self-destruction whenever you see it in other people or in yourself." He replied, "No, there is killing, suicide, murder, and people trying to do each other in. I think it is really a human meat market out there and nothing can be done." He could not yet allow himself to see that he was beginning to care about others, although he did acknowledge that he was beginning to love the dark young man. This is not unusual. Often when a therapist highlights the fact that a new behavior is evidence of a larger experience in forming, the patient blocks and refuses to recognize the presence of this forming (changing) because the possibilities it raises create anxiety. At other times, the individual may "lapse" into a negative appraisal of himself. Or he may forget the possibilities represented by the new events and only the constantly watchful eye of a good friend or therapist can alert him to the ways he is being different. Even with such stimulus, he may argue that a change is so little it is not worth noticing. Or he may argue vehemently that he is not changed at all and point to all the ways that he continues to destroy his life. He may take a secret pride in reiterating how destructive he is to his own best interests.

One patient of mine, Marvin, for example, came to practically every session with me complaining about all the ways he was not being helped. He would insist, in a whining tone, that he had not changed, despite the fact that it was clear that he was enjoying his life much more than ever before. He had become interested in fishing and we spent many hours in therapy talking about his new techniques and the fish he caught. I remember he reported that the first time he got a bass on the line he became so frightened of his potential success that he managed to let the fish get away. But subsequently, he talked proudly of the ramifications of bringing in fish and of how he had become an expert in gently playing them on the line. Still his complaining went on. One day I became quite annoyed. I told him I thought he was a mean and destructive person. "The fact is," I said, "you have changed." I pointed out that he was now able to sleep nights without sleeping pills, had managed to sit at his desk and write several chapters of a novel he had been projecting for ten years, and was having his first real relationship with another person. At first, Marvin was frightened by my anger. Then he agreed that perhaps there were some kinds of events in which he was more organized for himself. But, he said, he had "forgotten" all of these as he became frightened of the possibilities they offered. As he talked, there was a visible relaxation of his entire muscle structure and demeanor. The acknowledgment of the facts of what had happened over the course of our work provided relevant feedback which told him he had more capacity than he thought. He left the session stating that he felt stronger and more firm about what he was.

SHAPING NEW FORMS

The accumulation of incipient processes leads to the development of separate functions. There is an evolution of these functions toward the objectives inherent in their structure: hands are used for manipulations of the objects; thinking is for organizing the diversity of experience; interpersonal relating serves to enlarge experience. In the last instance, interpersonal relating, a person may feel a novelty in therapy when he sees he can like the therapist and live with these feelings of liking without having to be with the therapist twenty-four hours a day. As an incipient event, this realization shows him that people can have separate lives and still have a regard for one another. This form of relating may be different from the previous form of relating the person knew in which symbiotic merging was necessary in order to prevent the uncertainty of caring and being vulnerable. Another type of patient may feel a novelty in the different way he is received in therapy—that he is taken simply, as a person in process. This is different from his usual feeling of the world as critical (the way we saw Mrs. M. feel), a concept he has developed to handle novelty in a rigid form.

As we have observed, in the case of Patient B, the special functions of the use of hands and the capacity to talk to people organized to generate the possibility of going to medical school. There was a connecting with more parts of the organism (and the world) and a mobilization of those parts into their separate goals. Previously, B exhibited an exaggerated intolerance for novelty. If he experienced involvement with his work or another human being, particularly a woman, he would become overrun with tension. To relieve this tension he would go into a specific pattern of behavior in which he would hold his urine until it was "forced" upon him to let it go in his pants. In effect, he arranged an orgiastic pressure which forced him out of his tension by a supreme self-denigration. He then defecated in his pants, sometimes standing on his head so it would fall into his face. Both acts he preferred to perform in public so as to feel he was doing something against the rules. He would go out riding on his bicycle and allow the feces to come out in his pants. Sometimes he would wear a long overcoat and wear pants with a hole in them.

B experienced the development of tension as an imposition on his unlimited power. Actually, it was an imposition on the system he had developed which enclosed him and prevented him from processing novelty. He followed these acts with ritualistic masturbation. Again, he was rebelling against the rules. Masturbation released him from self-debasement through self-abandonment. It also allowed an experience in arousal, forming, and novelty which opened his capacity. After the masturbation, he relaxed, having returned to himself with some sense of possibility to be. These acts had numerous meanings for B. He liked to feel the feces between his legs like—as he imagined it—the soft down of a woman's pubic hair. It was a touch of warmth in his rigid cold world. He felt at one with woman and his feminine feelings while feeling the warm feces. Being at one with a woman, he felt, he denied the distinction of male-female since it made him both; it also dissolved the interest he had in woman which was a novelty that created tension because he felt it must be organized in a certain way if he was to avoid the uncertainty "woman" was *for him*. Being one with woman and then masturbating was his complete immersion (disorder) in all of the novelties he feared. He was not experiencing uncertainty, but instead "giving himself over to it". He traversed the inferno of uncertainty and did not die. Similar events followed any interest he took in laboratory experiments. At those times, he felt arousal, the possibility of change, and immediately experienced the association that "if I was to become too deeply interested I would be all alone in life". His fear of being alone was his expression of the constant terror he felt of being into a state of arousal-novelty-demand. This is felt, by all of us, as "being alone".

As incipient processes made themselves evident, there was a development of separate functions around the objective of attending medical school; this allowed for communication among various parts of B's system. Previously these were isolated and disconnected. He often found himself in new situations which he did not feel he could handle. He did not have available pathways for connecting his capacities. He had to fall into a self-abnegating pattern to integrate whatever abilities he had. He urinated, masturbated, and defecated with a sense of completion and he did not have to endure the tension of uncertainty about the results. He also avoided the male-female dilemma in these ways. The completed act, and the movement against the rules of society led to specific connections and to confirmation of himself as a unit, a state which he did not achieve when left on his own to organize novelty. When he was on his own, his pathways were blocked and he was a dispersed set of independent and unconnected parts.

The development of communicating pathways is one of the most interesting aspects of the stage of incipient processes. Patients have been in a bind, automatically falling into rigid patterns of behavior. Novelty demands; primarily it demands the opening of new pathways, and most patients move immediately to closure.

Harry reports to me that he is enjoying being alone. His girl friend is out of town and he feels it is a great opportunity to get more into his own experiencing. He will not "have to be responding to her". He will have more time to be quietly appreciative of his own rhythms. In the session following this, however, Harry finds himself in a state of distress. He observes that he has spent the last two days thinking only about how his girl friend is imperfect. His form has become a continuum: criticism. The state of being alone and with himself is experienced with considerable anxiety. He is unable to be there as he is, to be open to his own possibilities. Thus, he moves to a form of criticism. This is closure—it is a repetitive form. As we talk together in the session, he feels into the fact that his general patterning—overall structure—is to form relationships as a protection for himself. As long as he is with someone, he feels he does not actually confront the world alone. He organizes around the other. Harry's criticism of his girl friend arises out of discordant and disorganized feelings. Unable to follow the usual plan (her), he responds by forming "against her" and again creating her as the plan, albeit negatively. Thus he is still employing a mode of forming-by-using-relating, organizing around another person. The criticism involves an implicit recognition that this plan has failed to organize him for himself. The boundary-feel of knocking up against her in his mind forms a sufficient, but disturbing organization. It does not provide the necessary relief because he knows he is still alone and new processes of aloneness keep coming into the foreground (as B keeps meeting women). We work over this in the session. The next morning he awakens for the first time feeling free from the orgy of criticism, but is quite anxious. By afternoon, he "almost" calls me because he thinks he is going crazy. Later he becomes quite depressed. These responses are his direct experience of integrating. The depression is his deeper knowledge that he is the one doing the forming, and that ultimately it is to himself that he must turn. For Harry, being alone and *not* automatically involving himself in the form of using another person leads to his experiencing the uncertainty of his aloneness. One aspect of this is the opening of the pathway between the form—his driven behavior—and its contrast—the non-driven possibility. The parts which are formed as the whole of his being as "the driven to relate" could be reshaped, when it becomes clear to him that they *were* a shape; thus, Harry expressed his experience as a discovery that "I could be different, I actually do have some other possibilities for my life than living only according to the way this and that person determines my reality."

One of my patients in the incipiency period referred to herself as a soufflé. She said, "I feel I am getting to know myself, I know where I am at, and my feeling is it needs a gentle cooking to bring it to its proper development." During this period, she was becoming closer to her own feeling, and, simultaneously was becoming aware of her old, rigid forming.

CHAPTER 5

Control Processes and Aspects of New Forming

As we have observed,* a recently evolved neuropsychological model[1,2,3,4] suggests that the organization of behavior is a subtle connection of various control processes. Neuropsychologists have shown us that the visual recognition of an object is an active assembly of the basic features of the object. These may be the significant edges, colors, or protrusions. Recognition is a matching of an internal representation, gleaned from past experiences, with the object as perceived. The internal representation and the features operate together to subtly control the shifts of attention. The activity of perception follows the "reality" features in a scanning path influenced by the internal representation. The nature of the shape and direction of the immediate perception is determined. Moreover, the direction of the *probe* of long-term memory will be determined by the previous experience and forms that the organism has used for searching old records.

Ruth A., for instance, is unable to organize her feelings. She feels tyrannized by men. Every perception of a man is initially converted into the man being out to harm her. The minutiae of her visual and emotional experiences are cast into this form.

Mental and emotional control processes include coding, imaging, decision, rules, organizational schemes, retrieval strategies and problem solving techniques. Each of these is a form of integrating concrete particulars. A break in these control processes can either lead to the experience of disintegration and terror *or* to the excitement of new possibility. The capacities the person has developed and brings to the situation will determine which will be the case.

EXPERIENCING THE PARTICULARS

One patient wrote[37]:

We take for granted the knowledge of spaciousness and distinctness of our surroundings. But at first all we knew of space was what our limbs could reach. Sense data from our moving limbs, received and coordinated in the brain, give us a three dimensional map of our immediate environment, to this was added information interpreted with growing skill from a pattern of sense impressions received on the small curved surface of each retina. It is, when we think of it, a fabulous mental feat that we can interpret the tiny patterns received through the

*In Chapter 2.

lenses of our eyes, enlarge them and project them outwards in imagination so that they correspond with our three dimensional environment.

Ordinarily we fail to wonder at these processes. However, this patient, having been for so long submerged and perceptually dead, appreciates the wonder of having vision. We are reminded of Helen Keller: when she discovered the use of naming, she ran around wildly, asking her teacher to give everything a name. A patient in psychoanalysis may have the same opening wonder at the immense possibility of life. There is an exuberance which is often quite specifically interested in the *particular*. One man I saw in therapy tasted the doughnut taste from his childhood again. It arose in a moment of being uncritical of self. Suddenly feeling he could live in uncertainty as he was, he could allow forming to emerge. It did so first in the form of a past process. There was a new relationship between his immediate perceptions and past memories as there was a new form to his "reality". He stopped being compulsively protective of himself. For the first time, his form allowed for forming and thus the retrieval of a sensory moment of the past which reflected his current openness to sensory being. In psychoanalysis, we frequently see that a shift in the rules of searching permits more and more emergence of the past. New memories reveal a new perspective on earlier times. A new frame of reference leads to the recall of events that had been previously "forgotten".[5] Or what was previously seen only vaguely is now seen in its particulars: with more of the people involved, and more of the intimate circumstances.

There are significant differences in this process between schizophrenic patients and those other groups of patients, like neurotics, who are less damaged. Shakow[6] writes about schizophrenic patients that "there is a distinct weakening of the control center that serves integrating and organizing function of the interrelated cognitive, affective and conative processes, and makes possible the establishment of 'generalized' or 'major sets'." He comments that this is a result of "direct positive need to establish minor sets, to segmentalize both external and internal environments." For example, Ruth's set was her belief that she was tyrannized by men.

Elkes,[7] another researcher into this process, summarizes his findings as follows: the schizophrenic shows 1) the disturbance and fragmentation of association; 2) excessive concretization of thinking; 3) lack of appropriateness and modulation of affective response; 4) inability to maintain a state of readiness or response to incoming stimuli.

When a schizophrenic's form of organizing breaks down, the form that breaks is what we have called the form against forming. Then, as we have seen, what is labeled "psychosis" is in fact a state of being cast into a crucible of forming and processing. For most other patients, such as neurotics, the experience of the breakthrough into forming allows for a coordination of the current particulars with a past, or long-term memory store, which includes early experiences of making form. As children, neurotics could manipulate objects and have continuing sustained relating processes to other human beings. It was in more complicated interpersonal situations that anxiety necessitated the closed forms of neurosis. The schizophrenic patient, on the other hand, has had almost no positive early experience with open forming. When he is in the disorder of breakdown (psychosis), he cannot search previous memories for other possible schemes to employ.[8]

Arieti[9] has called attention to the fact that the thinking of the schizophrenic is involved in a phantasmic world where paleologic is predominant. In the paleologic form of cognitive structure, there is logic in which identity is based on predicates rather than subjects. There is also adualism, an inability to distinguish between the reality of the mind and that of the external world and there is acausality, a lack of appreciation of the cause and effect form of thinking we employ in our Aristotelian world. Parts are taken for whole, and verbalization may take on magical significance. Until the moment of psychoses, this lack of cognitive control capacity of the schizophrenic has been obscured by his highly developed imitative capacity. His internal representation has not been developed in experience but has been forced on him by the family. Schizophrenics learn to manipulate the symbols used by most adult members of their world, but have seldom actually grasped, experientially, the real meaning of such forms. Vygotsky[10] and Piaget[11] have both noted an analogous phenomenon in children. A child can be taught to imitate certain linguistic forms, but until he has evolved, through experience, the structural understanding that is necessary for such concepts as cause and effect and reversibility, he cannot use the language for meaningful transformations of his experience.[12,13,14] When the form against forming breaks down, the schizophrenic begins to experience the particulars of his existence and is caught in a terribly difficult position. He is deficient in control processes and when he needs to organize his particulars, there are no strategies available to him. That is one of the reasons for the appearance of so many bizarre forms in the psychotic event; because the patient is rapidly attempting to integrate, forming is at its peak and many forms are being tried.

At the Harvard Medical School, David Hubel[15] and his associates have shown, as mentioned,* that the deprivation of form-vision to new-born kittens results in a total lack of responsiveness in the cortex to stimuli from the retina of that eye. Interference with the ability to see in adult cats fails to result in any abnormality, indicating that as age progresses, flexibility is lost. This experiment indicates that deprivation severely affects developing systems and affects to a much lesser degree systems already present. In the study of Hirsch and Spinelli,[16] cats were raised from birth with one eye seeing vertical lines and one eye horizontal lines. The receptive areas of the cortex which responded to light from the horizontally conditioned eye responded only to horizontal signals; the receptive area of the vertical eye only responded to vertical signals. This, again, would seem to imply that the visual system is a function of training.[17]

*Chapter 2.

Various investigators[18,19] have insisted that the schizophrenic does not have developed control function, but since ordering of some sort is characteristic of every aspect of nature, it seems unwarranted to conclude that the process we call schizophrenia does not have a developed control. *Rather, it seems more likely schizophrenia has a different form of control.* In fact, what is involved, as described, is a behavioral form of control which closes off certain possibilities of interaction, with a resulting distortion of the general orientation in the world. With arousal, however, this form breaks down and the schizophrenic is opened to the various features of his perceptions, but they are features which lack the usual guides of internal representation. For change to occur, the schizophrenic must begin to "learn" how to see in new forms; he must develop his internal representations from scratch.

BEING THERE

As the process of engaging reality occurs, there is a move toward confronting the problems of being in the world. One schizophrenic patient, quoted by Laing, said[20]:

It's like a child or animal suddenly confronted–or being aware of–an adult's experiences for him, for instance, the grownup person has experienced a lot in their lifetime, they've built up gradually their capacity for experiencing life and looking at things–and, er–understanding them, even experiencing them for kinds of reasons, for aesthetic reasons, for artistic reasons, for religious reasons, for all kinds of reasons we experience things, which for–if a child or an animal, say, were suddenly confronted with these things they are not strong enough, they haven't got the equipment to do it. And I was facing things then that I just hadn't got the equipment to deal with, I was too soft, I was too vulnerable.

This man feels a deficit in his perceptual capacity. However, his words express his moment by moment engagement and the accompanying sense of vulnerability. The "willingness" to be there is the beginning of the power to integrate. The opening of pathways of information-flow among the parts of the organism creates a process. This has always been potential but now is actual. The feeling is of centralization. The person has a new perspective, perhaps best characterized as focus on the personal. The self-as-forming comes into being as the basic functions take on direction. What is now important, subjectively, is that the person must attend to his own experience rather than imitate other forms of thinking. Thus we hear statements like the following:

I thought I had come upon knowledge which other people do not have, knowledge which is obviously dangerous to have.[21]

That day was the day I began to move. Of course, I wasn't ripe for her sort of therapy yet, but I did react to that instant, overwhelming recognition of myself, my neurotic self X-rayed upon the page. I did exist.[22]

Patients of all kinds express this experience as a sudden illumination.[23] It is as if for the first time, they have become aware that they existed. The individual's previous form against form has been ego syntonic; he has experienced himself as incapable of being alive. He has not been aware of himself as an active participant in his life. He has been a process of "jumping" to organize every experience on the basis of a map he found available (learned) in his environment (family). This map includes directives which have told him not only what to think, but also how to feel and what to do.[24] With the clarification of connections among functions, there comes a realization of possibility of the self as a maker of form. The individual feels self-in-process; he senses that whatever direction emerges will have to be a combination of the forces of his unique history, environment, genetics, and so on.

REBIRTH

For the schizophrenic, this breakdown of old forms and opening of new ones is experienced in special ways. Boisen[25] writes:

In the initial stages, schizophrenic thinking follows a fairly definite pattern. After a period of preoccupation and sleeplessness, ideas begin to come as though from an outside source. This dynamism is a normal one. It is known as the "inspiration" or the "automatism", and may be defined as the idea or thought process which after a period of incubation darts suddenly into consciousness. In the case of the schizophrenic, because of the depth of the emotional stirring and the intensity of the concentration, such ideas come surging in with particular vividness. They seem to be entirely different from anything he ever thought or dreamed before. He assumes, therefore, that they come from a superhuman source. He thinks God is talking to him, or perhaps the devil is on his trail. In any case he feels himself in the realm of the mysterious and the uncanny. All the accepted basis of judgment and reasoning are gone. He does not know what to believe. His state is one of utter perplexity regarding the very foundations of his being. "Who am I? . . . What is my role in life? What is this universe in which I live?" become for him questions of life and death. Very commonly his eyes are opened to the fact that he is more important than he had ever dreamed. It "comes to him", or "something tells him" that a great responsibility has been resting upon him, and that his failure has brought untold misery to those whom he loves. Perhaps the entire world has been hanging in the balance, its fate dependent upon him. He has failed and it (the world) is about to be destroyed, but there may yet be a chance to save it. To do so he must sacrifice his own life. The readiness to make that sacrifice is commonly followed by a sense of being identified with God or with Christ. It may come to him that he is about to be reborn, or that he lived before in previous incarnation. Such ideas are common in the acute phases of schizophrenia.

Anton Boisen has lived through several psychiatric experiences and did numerous studies of other patients. One must place particular value on the statements of those people who have made the trip into disorganization and returned. They have experienced the awkward and frightening pain of traveling without a compass and in the dark of emotional formlessness.

Boisen stresses the qualitative sense of inspiration. Some schizophrenics, in an effort to concretize or organize the free flow, say their newness is from God;

others feel themselves in contact with the intimate sources of Being. Both of these responses suggest that some creative process is present.[26] Nature is an abundance of forming and forms. Similarly, these patients, too, are making forms and are experimenting with new ways of integrating.

Generally, with the movement into forming, there is a *sense of rebirth*. The disintegration of the old system and the connection with active processes is registered as "coming alive". Jordan Scher[27] has observed that schizophrenic patients have suffered, in early childhood, not from too much pain but from too little. They have been separated from the active confrontation with the problems of existence because the autonomy expressed in active confrontation would have been too threatening to the family system. The schizophrenic has not engaged the painful uncertainties of his family's conflicts. John Kafka,[28] for example, has called attention to the avoidance of paradox in schizophrenic families.

Hite[29] has noted a rebirth phenomenon similar to that of the schizophrenic in medical and surgical patients threatened by life-destroying diseases. She points out that patients may go through a disintegration and total remobilization of the organism in the process of coping with the stress of the disease. The entire event seems to bring the patient into greater contact with his basic processing of reality.[30] He has been a form of being to which he was clinging. But with the advent of the life-threatening situation, he is into a novelty which he must integrate with whatever assets he has. For these patients, their lives seem to come alive. Kelman[31] has observed similar events in the "Kairos" phenomenon.

Symbols of purification by fire and water run through much of the talk of Hite's patients; among psychiatric patients, some of the most frequently encountered symbols are those connected with the Christ myth and the Messiah process.

One patient I treated, Bill, would often leave an analytic session and walk down the street feeling "aglow". He felt good. He felt kindness toward the whole world. He was sure he had a kind and benevolent expression on his face. In these moments, it would "sneak" through to his consciousness that he felt "like Christ". He was sure people he passed on the street were wishing they could be in his company because of how good he was. The sessions which resulted in these feelings usually involved a lessening of Bill's self-hate and an upsurge of believing that he could trust his own feelings and his relationships with others. The sessions usually also involved some moments of letting himself be with me, as the analyst, without his usual suspiciousness, moments similar to what Erikson calls the moments of "basic trust".* In the analytic process, Bill

---

*In Erikson's theory,[32] this stage of basic trust is the time when the infant is involved in fundamental reflex processes. It is a time when connection to the modes of being are non-verbal, when the child is constantly forming at a body-oriented level. Trusting at this stage is a sharing of similarities, of being with the other–the mother–more than ever in life, as an *identity* of the self with other. Both mother and infant are being in the universe processing a shared reality with similar human functions.[33,34,35,36]

was accepting himself as a person with particular feelings. As he did, he was trusting what he could be and could do. I was there with him as he moved through the anxiety, making myself available if it became impossible for him to work with the uncertainty alone. As a child, Bill had not gone through a stage of basic trust. I knew my interventions were different from the way he reported his mother's had been, in that I did not insist that he do things the way I did and I did not feel particularly uncomfortable if he was anxious: I could tolerate his exploration. I knew from what he had told me that his mother could not do that. Specifically, my help at times of anxiety was to suggest that perhaps he might try to live in it or try to solve the problem in some different way. I could encourage Bill to try anxiety out, which I knew his mother could never do. She panicked if he was alone and quickly found ways to take him "out of this trouble". When he was alone as a boy, she would arrange activities or rush in to play a game with him. Bill's anxiety or restlessness was terrifying to her and thus it became so for him. As he gradually learned to give into this state and found he could operate in a reasonable way in it, he felt he was coming alive for the first time. Life was possible, and trusting himself, he felt "like Christ".

More disturbed patients, those who proceed into the experience we call schizophrenic psychosis, may become involved more directly with the Christ issue. They do not have the long-term memory store for transforming experience and the psychotic event is the first real experience in forming. They know that Christ was someone who was reborn. They form their event to mean that they *are* Christ. Bill had some memory of himself as a child, being at least partly integrated with his own feeling: he had, at an early age, through his own efforts, performed a few tasks which had yielded feedback which established that he was the alive coordinator of his activities. The acutely schizophrenic person has not had such moments and thus he experiences a rebirth which seems to him a birth. One patient wrote[37]:

I had now accepted as historically true the account of the Resurrection of Jesus given in the Gospels: if such an event had happened once it had set a precedent. There seemed no reason why if circumstances justified it, a similar event should not occur again.

Resurrection is a metaphor of all rebirth processes. This patient realizes, for the first time in her life, that she is an active member of the species. In that fact, she is a Christ who is a new and redeemed existence. Christ is an example and manifestation of God's power, the power of the creative forces in the universe. Through this symbol, she realizes the significance of her new being in the world.

TIME AS FORM

The form of organization is represented in characteristic modes of experiencing time.[38,39] This is evident with Bill's mother who could not tolerate her child's restlessness. Her system was constructed in fear of time as time, since time, at some level of being, is always experienced as the primary vulnerability of being human, the uncertainty of the ever-changing moment. Bill's mother lived in a structure which was an attempt to avoid the flow of process through a repetition of the past.

"Normally", that is, for most of us, every event is registered against its fit into the expectation of a plan. If expectation is not met, there is an implicit demand on the system for a reorganization in reality. In the neurotic and schizophrenic, the demand of novelty creates the usual initial disorganization of the structure. But instead of moving to try different forms—as most people do—they attempt to remain in their well-worn structure, and so, in effect, attempt to freeze themselves in time. For example, George asks his wife to do him a favor. He wants her to pick up a book for him at the library when she is downtown. She refuses and he becomes enraged. As we talk about it in our session, it becomes clear he has not just asked his wife to do the favor: he feels entitled to have her do it for him because he is doing her favors all the time. His is a structure of expecting her to do for him as he does for her. His activity toward her is not, for the most part, out of the feeling he has for her, but is part of his "deal" with her. He says, "I want her to do it, I feel she should, I am entitled." Throughout the discussion, he accentuates the "I", the permanent timeless concept of his self, the set on which he was basing his so-called identity. As we talk, he realizes this and then begins to see that his claim on his wife is an avoidance of her. She does not always act as she did today. "I am not facing," he says, "the question of why she is acting like this today. What kind of person would say no? Where is she at today, as far as her own feelings are concerned." In other words, what is her process?

Being more open to these dilemmas of the process of his wife, he remembers that it was an anxiety-provoking appointment she was going to and that she was feeling harassed having to be somewhere to pick up their kids shortly thereafter. George becomes poignantly aware that being open to these factual dilemmas of his wife means he will have to be integrating and open to changing his permanent concept of "I". His identity will have to be more fluid. He will have to relate to the facts and this "work", "openness", and "responsiveness" will call for being in time with all the vicissitudes of moment to moment alertness to what he feels and what the other feels.

When a situation of the neurotic or schizophrenic does not fit the expectations he has of himself, he does not engage the novelty of the way he is. Instead, he berates himself for not being as expected. The assumption is that the fixed structure reflects the way things are and that the actuality is an error. In other words, there is faulty ability to test reality, as well as a fear of time. For example, a patient may notice he is changing. He may see that he can act more in accordance with his own wishes and is less in the control or wishes of others. But immediately, he becomes resentful at feeling himself a part of a learning process. He "should have known before" is the way he expresses it. Actually, participation in learning frightens him because it is open to time and the moment by moment possibility of being different from the way he "thinks" he is. Similarly, a patient may realize how deeply he feels he is the greatest writer, cook, or doctor in the world and will begin to talk of how much he does not want to give up his notions of what a special person he is. With amazing regularity, I hear statements like the following·

If I give up this idea I have about myself, I will have to face that I am *just* a human being. Being human means terrible things to me: it means I will have to be involved in living, in the nitty-gritty of worrying about eating and feeling and working and other people, in day to day process. I will have to see my failures and I will have to know how much I want and that I have to try if I am to get what I want. It means I will have to be in time, in personal evolution and in participation. Ugh!!!! I can't stand it, I can't stand being human because if I am human, I will die—if I can die, that is terrible, it makes me feel so weak and so vulnerable. I have always believed I was immortal.

With the emergence of new control processes, a new relationship to time is established. The patient may begin to give special attention to each moment and to observe changes. He may start to carefully watch people or things for shifts in feeling and mood. He may begin to look for meanings behind every form and action. One woman wrote[40]:

I had been considering time past in its astronomical vastness, and seeing evolution as a visible development in my imagination. I watched it as one might watch a film taken of the opening of a flower, where the speeding up of a picture makes the blossom appear to move and open up before your eyes.

Time is an experience for her of the particularity of her past as well as the past of the human species. It is appreciated in its personal and its universal dimensions. The metaphor of a flower conveys the sense of the opening out of her personality and the slow emerging evolution of her being. Another wrote[41]:

Time means so much and we do not have time to wait around or just kill time; time is money and we have to use time to the best advantages. God help us to use our time more usefully than we have in some of our time in the past.

The shift in the experience of time is an appreciation of the underlying continuum of existence. Frequently, a patient may recognize that his life in time has been artificial. He may come to see that he is, in fact, in time, by simply being alive, but that the daily modes of his occupation, his talking, his buying things, etc., are his way of being "out of time". He knows he has been afraid to confront his pure, still existence and he finds himself letting go: he sees the compulsive modes of forming in which he has indulged. He experiences—at first only for brief moments, then more frequently—the possibility of not having to do or be anything. He feels, often ecstatically, the joy of simply being. Time becomes the potentiality for living in the openness and vulnerability of the changing moment. These are profound moments in the transformation of the personality.

Part III

THE REVOLUTION AGAINST THE OLD FORM

CHAPTER 6

The Family as the Ground of Revolution

A revolution begins with the experience of vulnerability and impotence. By letting himself go into the state of arousal, brought on by novelties both inner and outer, a person begins to have an awareness of his *potency* and his concomitant human *impotence* in the uncertainty of time and change. With the experience of vulnerability, the involvement with organizing reality through trial and error begins.

STRUCTURE OF A REVOLUTION

Thomas Kuhn,[1] in his brilliant work, *The Structure of Scientific Revolutions*, has described a revolution in science as a slow struggle for the articulation of a new fact. It "is necessarily a complex event, one which involves recognizing both *that* something is and *what* it is". The structure of a scientific revolution is, in several ways, analogous to that of a personality revolution and may shed some light on the problems.

Kuhn points out that Roentgen found that a barium platinocyanide screen glowed when his cathode ray tube worked. He did not expect this event and it violated fixed notions and expectations about the way things were. It led Roentgen to retreat into his laboratory for seven weeks of day and night work to ferret out the facts and the meaning of this new event for the understanding of things. Kuhn writes:

> Though X-rays were not prohibited by established theory, they violated deeply entrenched expectations. Those expectations, I suggest, were implicit in the design and interpretation of established laboratory procedures. By the 1890's, cathode ray equipment was widely deployed in numerous European laboratories. If Roentgen's apparatus has produced X-rays, then a number of other experimentalists must for some time have been producing those rays without knowing it. Perhaps those rays, which might well have other unacknowledged sources too, were implicated in behavior previously explained without reference to them. At the very least, several sorts of long familiar apparatus would in the future have to be shielded with lead. Previously completed work on normal projects would now have to be done again because earlier scientists had failed to recognize and control a relevant variable. X-rays, to be sure, opened up a new field and this added to the potential domain of normal science. But they also, and this is the more important point, changed fields that had already existed.

Roentgen had faith in his discovery; he continued with the process of its elucidation, despite the resistance from colleagues who called it a hoax. He experienced the discordance; he worked to understand the relationship between all the old facts and the new one. And once the relationship to the new fact was clarified, the old facts looked different.

THE PERSONALITY REVOLUTION

The personality revolution expresses itself in many different forms. The organization of the initial experience of novelty reflects the kinds of structures which are being interrupted. In the personality revolution, as with Roentgen and his discovery, the new fact must bring with it the realization of old facts in new positions. For instance, whereas before a patient may have believed his brother was a weak, sad, maligned person, he can now begin to see his brother is using his sadness to get others to feel sorry for him. He can begin to see his brother as a man in a world of men and women, a man with his own history and functions, someone to appreciate in many contexts. This opens up an entirely new and revolutionary perspective.

The primary arena for the personality revolution is usually the family. A human being is a developing process in the ground of the family unit which in turn is grounded in society. The family itself is an arrangement of modes of being in the society.

The family has goals and rules which are functions of the basic attitude of the parents about being, people, life and time. In this milieu, a child has a position with respect to the other members of the system and with respect to the ways the total system orients itself to the cosmos. Usually the mother and father are the programmers of the way the child relates to the world. The way they feel about their own being in the world will be mirrored by the child since a child feels about people and the process of being a person in general as he feels about those close to him. And often, particularly in highly neurotic and schizophrenic family systems, the feeling that he has, however well concealed, is one of impotence. I have frequently found with patients that even in situations where they have been considered to have identified with a powerful parent over the impotent one, deeper investigation reveals that they have, in fact, seen themselves in the impotence of the weaker, as this is revealed in their own deep feelings of impotence. Of course, true power in its openness to both weakness and strength would be beyond such identification processes because it allows for the actual recognition of vulnerability and struggle. But this true kind of power emerges only if rigid plans to manage reality are given up in favor of systems which open the self to the spontaneous evolutions of capacity.

IMPOTENCE

In a revolution, a patient often focuses on the mother and the feelings about her. In part, this is an expression of the essential differentiating process. Mrs. O., as a child, spent many hours with her mother walking down Flatbush Avenue on Saturday nights. Together they would look longingly at the clothes in department store windows.

> We were involved in an orgy of self pity, feeling sorry for ourselves that we did not have money to buy the clothes. We were also enjoying that we did not have the clothes because we were hating my father who made it impossible for us to live and possible to hate. We thrived on this hate and self pity.

Mrs. O. felt together with her mother in a mutuality of weakness and life-avoidance. The mother repeatedly communicated her life story to her. The mother emphasized that she had been an orphan. She complained that no one knew how terrible it was to be without a mother except an orphan; Mrs. O. was instructed to take note and to be grateful that she had a mother—to be careful never to risk jeopardizing that relationship. Mrs. O's lifelong compulsion to possess and own things was, then, an aspect of her mother's feelings of never having had a mother or enough love. Mrs. O. could not be in the present as it was uncertain; she had to *have* and to be moving toward *having* at all times. Whenever I gently suggested a distinction between herself and her mother, she would become acutely anxious and disorganized for five to ten minutes. One time I told her she seemed to like her father even though the mother hated him. When I said this, she could not stay still, and began to smoke incessantly; she said she felt like she was "losing her mind". On one occasion after I had made such a remark, she called me the next day saying she was unable to get out of bed; every move was a cause of dizziness and nausea. A full-blown Meniere's syndrome was diagnosed by her physician. This indicated how intimately connected she was with her mother. Later in her therapy, when she could separate a bit from her mother, she spoke of being "afraid" to separate because she would be an orphan like her mother. She would be vulnerable and alone.

In her revolution, Mrs. O. focuses on the mother and the feelings about her. In part, this is an expression of the essential differentiating process. She has not learned to confront reality with her own being and the mother may have never learned to confront reality with her own capacities. So together mother and child have been living in a symbiotic matrix of avoiding novelty. In separating from the mother, the patient engaged in a reality process and tried to extricate herself from the family myth which had developed around the paucity of being. The rules in Mrs. O.'s family systems stressed the importance of steering clear of novelty because the mother could not tolerate its demands. Thus, avoidance modes of organization prevented or attenuated any process which created arousal; this meant that Mrs. O. had to avoid the experience of time, change, paradox, and hostility, but also tenderness through her early life.

Mrs. O.'s need to have things and possess objects was, of course, being in time in a certain way, but primarily it was *not* being in time openly, allowing herself to happen, because that would expose her to feelings of impotence. She was being like her mother; if she was not "filled" or "moving to be filled", she felt exposed to reality. As we have indicated, in disturbed families, each member is implicitly instructed in the dangers of autonomy, since autonomy is a threat to the system's principal demand that everyone "stay together". This directive is frequently generated out of the family myth that one member is too weak to live. Everything must be done to protect that member from danger, and everything is dangerous for everyone because it is dangerous for that member. In Mrs. O.'s case, the mother feels this way about herself; she feels this way about living; she had a mother who felt life this way. The father feels this way about his mother and about himself and protects the mother-wife as a means of protecting himself. His union with her is, more often than not, a self-developed protection process. She protects him, he protects her; she absorbs his fear of being afraid. If he shows signs of independence, she accentuates his anxiety noting the dangers. This brings him back into fear. Or she may develop signs of her own fear, thereby demanding his concern if he strays too far afield.

The person who has felt unconsciously impotent, like Mrs. O., has had to move within very carefully determined boundaries. He has had to choose short-term goals and needed to be careful to require little commitment from others. Since he has been unable to trust himself to bring about any effective sequence of actions, he has secretly believed he could not engage in interpersonal or intrapsychic processes. Because he believed, unconsciously, that he could not affect the way his life developed, his life philosophy may have as its basic assumption that nature is organized by chance alone. He must believe that one can do nothing to influence his own fate. The forms that such people will use to dramatize and justify their faith in the meaninglessness of life are often quite remarkable. Sexual impotence is an operative example of a person who cannot engage in the vicissitudes of change.

A particularly good example of the way this family process of tacit hopelessness actually influences behavior can be seen in Mrs. O.'s feeling of impotence about handling money, a metaphor for or key to her general feeling of impotence. Mrs. O. was compulsively unable to choose how she wanted to spend her money, and was unable to save. She always had to have her checkbook with her because she could not engage the anxiety of being away from her home without it. When she became anxious, she could alleviate her pain by "buying some object to fill herself with something". She was completely unable to engage in virtually any open situation. She was phobic about elevators, planes, and high floors, any place where she felt she could not immediately escape. Inevitably, she would feel "trapped". These situations limited her freedom to escape; they demanded that she limit her compulsion for absolute freedom. They asked her to make a choice.

In the therapy, it was difficult to engage this process. My very help was a confirmation of her weakness and even if I said nothing, she felt helped, and therefore weak; from the other side, an interpretation was taken as a criticism of her capacities and, thus, also a support to her image of weakness. One day, I told her that she would be responsible for three sessions a week. Up until that point, I had not felt she would be able to meet such responsibility and would have found the anxiety too threatening. At this juncture, I was sure she could make use of such a therapeutic stance. I said no excuses were to be accepted. She became quite angry and said she was opposed to this. She would have to decide, she asserted, if she was paying for therapy or time. She began to explore her feelings about commitments and responsibility. She felt that my rule put the analysis on a different plane, one which she was not sure she wanted to move to. If she were responsible for three times a week, she had to realize that neither the analysis nor the dependency could go on forever. If the work had a limitation in time, that meant she had to begin to take more control of her life. Finally, she said that for the first time, she realized she had options and had to choose how she wanted to spend her time.

Mrs. O. had been constantly expressing her inability to deny herself her non-being. She was afraid of exposure in the state of choice and decision. The confrontation represented by my statement put her into direct connection with a limit. There in the session, her now firm relationship with me was a process which was undeniable. She was enough into herself to know her feelings of wanting to continue the analysis. With the limitation expressed, she was led to a process which broke the rigid behavior of not-being-there. Until this point, she had avoided actually facing the feeling of impotence which had arisen out of her family system and was being unconsciously expressed in her phobias. In confronting the real possibility of choice, she was confronting that impotence, and the identification with her mother.

Having compulsively avoided the pain of vulnerability, the patient inevitably knows that a new direction requires powers which are, as yet, undeveloped. This lack of developed power is, understandably, experienced as further impotence which is accompanied by rage, sadness, self-hate, depression, and fear.

People pursuing rewards contingent on their skilled behavior are able to adapt their plans of action to the goals which they have evolved.[2] A person who assumes the effectiveness of self-initiated action has a central notion of the competence of his system. When anyone can feel his competence, he is open to the next fact: the realization of his true impotence as a human being in the ever changing universe. It is this realization that a pride system, such as that of Mrs. O., seems most designed to oppose; it strives to prevent the flow of painful experiential uncertainty. In the flow of events, there is a constant recurrence of paradoxical moments. Every person is faced with the need to act and to organize these uncertainties. A glimpse of competence, and the underlying impotence, leads a patient into a confrontation with the essential and basic impotence of life: death.

Patient B said in a session that he was having difficulty in realizing "some people die." I noticed a note of contempt in his voice as he spoke of this sadly inadequate group of people who were so naive as to let that happen to them. I gently averred that he was correct, "It is true, some people die, one hundred per cent of them;" he became pale, then he blushed deeply and became quite anxious. He began to talk of his early terrors as a child and the terrific anxiety he had felt in being vulnerable to his mother's wrath. He recalled her yelling at him to go and get the pencil he had lost while running from a group of tough boys. He felt that she had no mercy, pushing him out of the family into that scene in which he had felt so inadequate. For him that moment of novelty, his awareness of his death, had become an arousal for orienting. This moment of seeing death broke through his organization in the family as a protected non-being and he was faced with the necessity for engaging. He began to have a minute but definite experience of self-clarification.

As patients remember their past in the family and discover their own needs and feeling, they often experience a painful sense of impotence as aloneness. Mrs. O. observed:

> I cannot always have what I want, but if I do have what I want, you, whoever the you may be, cannot always have what you want from me because then I will be first to me; but then too I cannot always have what I want from you if I realize you can have wants. But if you have wants then I realize you may respond by saying, "I do not need you all that much."

The great terror: that others do not need her. This confronts her with the aloneness and the powerlessness she feels when she experiences herself as a separate and autonomous creature. Her system has attempted to get others to be dependent on her. Now she sees this has been to avoid her fear of being alone. The moment after her statement, she flashes, with the incredible clarity of biological integrating, the image of herself as a three-year-old girl: her father is saying he will "no longer take her to the bathroom at night". She will have to get her mother to help. That image conveys her feeling alone outside the structure of the family. A colicky infant, the only way her discomfort could be assuaged during the first years of life was by sleeping on her father's stomach. In the first years of our work together, she had frequently commented that when she was a child, her father was "really her mother". In the flash, she pictured a major transformation in her life, the transition from being Daddy's little girl to being embedded with mother in a state of dependency. She realized her fantastic rage over that change. She had felt, and still feels, powerless to effect any action in any situation. She had given up trying to do or be what she wanted, had turned away from her own wanting, and had evolved patterns of connection with her mother which made her fear to be different from the mother in any way. If she felt different from the mother, she sensed a rising terror. The terror made her impotent. She kept telling me "the most fear I have is to feel I exist. As a child I began to feel I was a 'head', an observer with eyes. I did not exist because to exist would mean to know what I felt."

Recognizing the basic sense of impotence precipitates a revolution in awareness. This is often felt as a potency-in-action with future possibility.

Patient B, for example, kept being shocked to find he is a human being. As obvious as it sounds to most of us, to him it was a true discovery. On one occasion, B lost a chess game to a colleague. He told me later he had discovered that, for the first time, he was able to accept that he could lose and could still play more games in the future. "I realized that I was a man who worked in a laboratory and who was playing chess with a friend and lost; it was not a great chess master giving an exhibition game in a large hall." For him, the simplicity of being able to win and lose in any number of future games was a new and wonderful possibility. He felt he suddenly had the opportunity to play and improve his skill and did not have to look at every game as the proof or disproof of his being. He was a self in open process and could separate himself from the assumption that he had to be one way, and that anything else was dangerous. Put another way, he was accepting his vulnerability in time.

In the next session, B began to talk of some hoped for pleasures of having an apartment with a staircase. He said, "A staircase in a room gives the day an air of ampleness." It seemed clear that he was talking about himself and his new being. Before this, he had only dreamed of huge ornate rooms without staircases and with rigidly arranged furniture. This was another way in which he had been trying to protect himself, a pride system grandiosity which was part of, and analogous to, his illusion of being a grand master. During the period of incipient processes, B dreamed of a small, cramped, caved-in room with low ceilings, and spoke of it being as limited as he has been. At that time, he had just begun to feel the limitations involved in these grand expectations. Now in the revolution, he dreamed of an apartment with ampleness. He was expressing his freedom to move to different levels in a way that was the beautiful, poignant, and specific "a room with a staircase gives the day an air of ampleness".

Another case, which again shows that vulnerability is at the core of the revolution is that of an acute psychotic patient, R. I remember one day sitting on a bench in the hospital yard with R. We had been working together for several months and that day I had decided we would go outside together. I bought two cups of coffee and we went to sit in the sun. Sitting there together, his eyes seemed to search me to the marrow of my bones to see if he could trust me. I noticed the entire muscle bundle around his mouth was quivering. It seemed clear that this was an experience for which he had no previous memory and one which he felt was a novel event. I was not just there, I was another person. I was a changing fact. Our work together had made it possible for him to begin to be in the forming process and to attempt to bring my concrete presence together with all the concepts he had about me. I was a doctor who had power over him; he felt many likings and many hostilities for me; I reminded him of others he loved and hated. All these conflicting and various features demanded his opening to new categories and called for using his capacity for category formation and generalization. He could move in that direction only very slowly. R had never known people who were not going to hurt him if he trusted them. He wanted to trust, but he felt he would evaporate if he gave up the self-protection he believed he had achieved in being withdrawn and "invulnerably" detached. At the age of six months, R had total body exzema to which his mother told me she had reacted with pain and disgust. To be trusting with me would mean again the experience of vulnerability and nakedness he doubtless felt in those early moments. He was afraid. Before he could evolve a faith in his own functions, he would have to expose himself to all that awkwardness and terror.

LEONARD

Actual revolution may appear suddenly, as was the case with a patient of mine, Leonard K., who had evolved to the point where he was now able to come to a dramatic realization about his place in the family system. Leonard's parents had come to visit him. During the visit, the father accused Leonard of not being respectful to his mother, who sat there passively looking hurt and mistreated. Leonard reported to me that he had suddenly screamed at his mother, "I hate you, I hate you, I hate you; you were never there for me and you pretended how much you loved me when you were only interested in yourself, yourself, yourself. You are a liar." He recalled that, suddenly, at the moment of screaming, he felt a complete and overwhelming sense of truth and honesty, unlike anything he had felt in his life before. He said many times subsequently, "That was the truest moment of my life; I will never do anything or make any decision that goes against that feeling of truth and knowing that what I was feeling was mine."

For the greater part of his life, Leonard maintained an ambivalent relationship with his mother. He wanted independence but was constantly experiencing a fear of it. He recalled that several times when he was young, he had spoken profanity to his mother. This was an indication that he was angry with her because he needed her, but also showed that he was trying to separate and grow. He recalled that once when he did this, she washed his mouth out with soap. "She let me know she was not interested in direct communication and since then we have not talked honestly to each other." On another occasion, Leonard remembered she had made him wait nude at bedtime so that she could tell the father of his day's misdemeanors. Then his father had given him a full-fledged beating. These events clearly communicate the structure of the mother's feeling about her child's separateness. As he evolved, Leonard could not differentiate his identity as distinct from his mother's. He was unable to confront experience alone, and he lived out his hesitancy through abortive efforts to separate psychologically. Thus, the mother was a reality and ground for his efforts at differentiation. She would say to him, "You do not love me," or accuse him of not saying "hello" everytime she walked in the room. When Leonard would hear this, he would cringe inside. The mother's accusation caught him in his effort to separate and he attempted to attentuate his independence by his integrative cringing. His fear collaborated with her desire to entangle him. But it led to more hate of her for exposing his fears of being separate.

For years, Leonard was unable to accept his hate of her, yet felt confused and would intrapsychically attempt to deny it. In a sense, he had to try to separate through hate because he was afraid of the openness the separation presented. Thus, he needed the violent act of screaming at his mother in order to "shake" himself free. In the moment of screaming, Leonard suddenly felt he was acting on his own behalf; the "no" to her was a "yes" to himself. He clarified suddenly that her clinging to him was an implicit assertion that neither of them could exist in reality. Now, in the instant of screaming, he was saying he could do without her and could be in the world without the family system. He was saying he believed he could be a different self from the one which he was to her and to himself when he shared the family idea.

The story of Leonard's confrontation with his mother demonstrates prerogatives of the system and the destructiveness which it carries out on its members. It also clarifies the role of a therapist in helping to direct the process of revolution.

The revolution had begun some months before the screaming incident with Leonard feeling illuminated about the father's position in the structure. Leonard had been receiving large sums of money from his father for many years. The family system defined this as the father doing Leonard a tremendous good turn, for which he was expected to be eternally grateful. On many occasions, the father told his son that he (the father) had never been able to do what he wanted in life. He discussed having always wanted to become a painter, but because he had the responsibility of his children, he had worked hard and "sacrificed" his life in order to make life easy for his kids; they were to live the meaningful life which he could not manage himself. The message of this communication was that the cosmic failure of the father was to be redeemed by the son's contribution to mankind. Leonard was encouraged to feel the father was stuck with the mother and *had* to stay with her to protect the children from her sickness. Another sacrifice. Leonard's behavior was supposed to prove worthy of the father's sacrifice in this area as well. All of this was conveyed in the spirit of how much was being done for Leonard and what a good and loving family they were. "They all loved each other and were good to each other." If anyone dared to do something for himself, a hue and cry went up of selfishness. I have found that in all families in which the structure of novelty-avoidance is present, there is an effort by the system to instill guilt when an autonomous act is made by one of the family members. Thus, each person feels "selfish" when he acts individually.

In our sessions together, Leonard began to see that much of his father's behavior was self-serving to the father's needs. Leonard saw, almost in a burst, that his father had been, in effect, paying him a salary to be nice to his mother, because the father desperately needed to keep her happy. As with Roentgen, when this fact became clear, all the other data took on a new perspective. He saw the father had been compulsively helping him to protect his (the father's) anxiety about being alive, and had, meanwhile, been demanding that Leonard express his gratitude by leaving the mother undisrupted. This meant being dishonest with her. But also, implicitly, and more importantly, it meant that Leonard was not to separate from her, as that would lead to her feeling discomfort. The family system thus served to perpetuate Leonard's dependency.

Separation had a special meaning in this context; it meant the right to feel openly hostile to the mother and to the family mythology. In the systems which breed rigid structures, the experience of separation will catapult the patient into an anxiety about aloneness, individuation, and autonomy. With every such patient I have ever worked, I have gone through something like the following: the patient will say, "I like such and such, but I am afraid to be liking it." What is this fear of liking? The patient answers: "I feel selfish," or "It scares me that I will get more and more involved in doing what I like." What is the danger about that? "It will lead to being alone and isolated. I will not need anyone and I will be out there."

The hostility generated in the revolution is multi-facted. After being afraid about separation, the patient becomes anxious and attempts to wrench himself loose. By employing a violent form of action, he can frequently convince himself he means what he says. His act is a beginning of feeling autonomy. He struggles against the tendency to give himself back into the dependency processes. The hostility acts to delineate him as separate. Because he still feels impotent, he is unable to allow for the open give and take involved in a true differentiation, which does not need to identify either negatively or positively with another person as the individual takes himself as is. But the revolution is the defining phase and the patient must make an initial distinction between himself and others in closed forms of action such as hostility before he can take himself separately in his own context.

A mother who cannot tolerate the uncertainty of reality is made particularly uncomfortable in the presence of a child who is attempting such hostile differentiation. The mothers convey the message that hostility and negative actions are not acceptable. The child frequently interprets this message as a dictum against separation and individuation. As hostility may be the only way the child can make his initial moves toward autonomy, the mother's attitude may be particularly damaging. In Leonard's case, Leonard's childhood hostility was obviously particularly dangerous to the mother. She would reportedly develop headaches, insomnia, and other physical manifestations of her pains whenever there was an argument or opposition to her by the father or by Leonard.

A child in Leonard's situation may internally absorb the negation of self which is entailed by the family's fears. Family process is itself an exceptionally closed system. The family's beliefs are considered by the child the only reality. With these as parameters, he learns the map of being. He does not realize that the behavior and beliefs of the other family members arise out of their needs. Clinging behavior, for instance, is elevated by the family system to a fact, a virtue, and a moral imperative. The parents are unable to say to their children, "I am afraid, I need you," or "I want you to stay with me." They say, "I am a good mother; I want only the best for you and thus I must watch what you do." In Leonard's case, the father said he was working hard for the child; he could not say that he *had* to work because he was afraid to be open to time and his own desires. The child is, therefore, faced with having to believe that he is responsible for his father's actions. He bears the burden for the father's misery. He feels responsible and in his guilt, he collaborates with the father's needs to conceal his (the father's) fear of being alive. The child feels excessively powerful, guilty, and overwhelmed for making the father act in this way. The child attempts to live out the father's demands and relieve himself at the same time, of this burden. He is thereby caught up in avoiding being for himself. This conforms to the overall plan of the family in which everyone is to avoid being for himself.

There is a deep and central source of confusion in this kind of family relating process. The young child feels that he is not loved for himself, yet the system asserts that all is love. Since he is being told to be a certain way, he tends to take and register this as meaning it is not all right for him to be himself, so he then begins to feel there is something wrong with him. One patient wrote[3]:

Oh, they love him, but they want him or force him or expect him to be different! *Therefore he must be unacceptable.* He himself learns to believe it and at last even takes it for granted. He has truly given himself up. No matter now whether he obeys them, whether he clings, rebels or withdraws his behavior, his performance is all that matters. His center of gravity is "them", not in himself—yet if he so much as notices it, he thinks it natural enough. And the whole thing is entirely plausible; all invisible, automatic, and anonymous.

In this state, a child gradually evolves a plan of behavior in which he is organized such that he does not trust the spontaneous expressions of his own experiences.

Leonard said to his father, "You have been paying me this salary to be nice to her." His father gasped, "You could have done nothing that would better have stabbed me in the heart."

Leonard had taken the life out of the entire lie and his father collapsed on the floor crying. He could not think and was dizzy. "My head just won't work anymore."

The father's reaction convinced Leonard that he had penetrated one of the secrets of his childhood. Having illuminated the familial need for denial of the mother's controlling-through-weakness, Leonard was then able to face the pure fact of the mother. In facing her, he experienced that ultimate moment. He came into clarity about his sense of impotence, the pain that it was for him, and its development out of his relationship with his mother. By extricating himself violently from his mother, Leonard was confronting his previous denial of his vulnerability, as well as the dishonesty of the lies and pretenses he had experienced in the family system.

Leonard's subsequent process called for particularly careful and delicate work on my part. The family structure began immediately to attempt a restitution. Leonard felt he had established his position. The father began to write him letters accusing him of being cruel and evil. I felt it was my task as therapist to clarify and confirm for Leonard that he was struggling to establish a sense of self. I stressed that he had to do it in this way because he felt uncertain about his capacities to differentiate himself from the family scheme. I believed I could best help by supporting his self assertion and by continually emphasizing that he was struggling to find his independence. I found with Leonard, as I have with other patients, that when I could clearly define the direction of his struggle as well as the parameters of its activity, he could more easily mobilize his efforts. With Leonard, I continually tried to help him reaffirm his new understanding of his parents' egocentricity. By doing this, I was supporting his awareness of the parental system's deception which called the parents' needs virtuous. He could then experience his feeling that his parents never cared for him. Thus, he could feel liberated from the guilt about not loving them the way they claimed they loved him.

As the Doctor in "I Never Promised You a Rose Garden"[4] says:

> You were asked to mistrust even the reality to which you were closest and which you could discern as clearly as daylight. Small wonder that mental patients have so low a tolerance for lies . . .

In sum, as we have seen, the duplicitous family situation had left Leonard unable to deal with his human impotence and vulnerability. With all this "love" there, Leonard ought to know he had support. Yet, in truth, it was never there when he felt unhappy, depressed, and uncertain. These were feelings which stimulated the anxiety of the parents and they would run from or deny his misery. Thus he knew there was no real help available in moments of true human vulnerability.

The real difficulties began for Leonard in his revolution when his father wrote him letters of accusation. Leonard would immediately fall into feeling guilty. He did not feel firm enough in his new position. In one of the letters Leonard showed me, the father wrote: "Your mother awakens at night screaming, 'What did I do?' Only you can help her and bring her out of this depression." Leonard knew this was the old tactic—to make him the one responsible and suck him back into a family system that denied all confrontation. After showing me the letter, Leonard said:

There it is again; Mother is depressed–it is as if no one else in the world is depressed–I have no feelings and no depression; nothing we said that night has any meaning, nothing that is, that I felt, only that she had the bad feelings from my acting as I did. Fuck her, that's what I say. The real fact is she is not supposed to feel anything, any sadness, because it makes him uncomfortable. He doesn't see anyone else's depressions; everyone else should mold themselves to make her happy. That son-of-a-bitch. I am reminded of when he came to see me once when I was first married. My wife had made an apple pie for the dinner for the three of us. His only comment was, Boy, you should taste the apple pie mother makes. I could have kicked him in the mouth. I wish I had.

Other letters came accusing Leonard of "being mean and cold". In one of them, the father claimed he had made Leonard everything he was and therefore Leonard ought to be grateful. This made the father's fundamental lack of respect for his son dramatically clear. But Leonard felt guilty whenever the accusations came. Still, he remained firm. He kept saying, almost as a self bolstering, that the moment of screaming at his mother was truest moment in his life and that nothing would make him go back on that. I continued to support him since I saw that the guilt he felt was a guilt about asserting himself. He had broken the rules of the family system. According to the family discussion that ensued, it was agreed (between the father and mother) that he must have been psychotic that night or somehow must have gone out of his mind. He had only to call up and apologize, admitting that he had lost his mind that night and all would be forgiven. He refused. But his guilt remained a problem during the next two years of therapy.

GUILT

The feeling of guilt is central to the structural revolution. But there are two forms of guilt which must constantly be carefully discriminated by the therapist. First, there is the kind of guilt from which Leonard was suffering, the guilt of having broken the rules of the system. In this form of guilt, patients feel a kind of inner flimsiness of their being. One patient I treated, for example, noted he felt his muscles dissolving so that he could not lift his arm. "It is soft, a kind of itchy warmness which goes up and down the arms and the inner abdomen seems to give way." It has been described by many as "wanting to merge back into the mother".

In contrast, the second kind of guilt is that in which the person feels he has wasted his life. He becomes aware of the various alienated forms he has employed to protect himself from anxiety and sees with painful clarity that he has been "running away from himself" without actually making contact with his basic feelings. Buber has called this "animating guilt". Phenomenologically, patients experience it very differently. They feel their arms are strong, the gut is firm, they are ready to face the emptiness of their past with the capacities they have. They begin to taste what they eat, and to feel increasing pleasure in their senses so that they more and more experience guilt about what has been missing. But they are now firm enough in themselves to see what they are not.

But of the first kind of guilt, the guilt over breaking out of the system, Perceval writes,[5] poignantly:

> I perished from a habitual error of mind, common to many believers, and particularly to our brethren and Roman Catholics, *that of fearing to doubt*, and of taking the guilt of doubt upon my sincerity; because we force ourselves to say we believe, because we think doubt sinful. Whereas, we cannot control our doubts, which can only be corrected by information. To reject only persuasion willfully is no crime, but to declare willfully that we believe what we doubt, or presumptuously that our doubts are willful is another.

First the guilt of doubt. The patient feels he is wrong to doubt the old system. Second, he considers forcing himself back into what he doubted. (Leonard's urge to write his parents and plead guilty.) Third, in rejecting the old system he feels he has committed a crime. It seems to Perceval this way, and certainly it seemed so to Leonard. But Perceval also expresses the concomitantly contrary feeling that is part of the awareness, namely, that it is a crime *not* to accept what has happened and continue to doubt the system. He is aware, as was Leonard, that he can never go back on his sense of truth.

Gregory Bateson,[5] in the introduction to Perceval's book, wrote:

> His (Perceval's) error, as I read it, was a failure of responsibility. He ought not to have glutted his pride and weighed his conscience by branding his "doubt" as "guilty". That he should have accepted as a function of the individual mind to be responsibly exercised. He ought to have taken the new responsibility or doubt upon his conscience.

The task of the revolution stage of process is to allow the patient to accept the responsibility for doubting the old structure. Doubt reflects the vicissitudes of a shifting organization. When we look at gestalt figures, such as the duck-deer, we often find ourselves moving back and forth between two visual organizations. In a similar way, the person involved in revolution moves back and forth between two ways of being in the world.

At this early stage, the therapist can participate in a positive thrust toward the new organization by defining the terms of the struggle. Often the ground of that struggle is the family. In Leonard's case, the family was his parents, but it can also be the marriage as an extension of the parental system.

A man fights with his wife over not wanting to take a vacation. He feels the struggle in the symbols of the particular problem. His wife is saying to him, "You never want to go away with me," and she is thereby attempting to use guilt (that he is breaking the rules of the system) to encourage him in her direction. He is only aware that he does not want to go and feels himself to be taking a stand against his cultural and social milieu (everyone they know takes a vacation). He feels confused and cannot understand the perspective. In our session, I am able to point out to him that he does not want to be exposed to his wife's anxiety. When he is alone with her, he feels absorbed by her difficulties. He feels her anxiety as something she is using to trap him and prevent him from attending to his own feelings. I am aware of his long-term struggle with this issue and can support his efforts by indicating that at this stage in his development he perhaps needs to say "no". It is necessary to give himself time to develop. It is also important for him to realize he need no longer be passively absorbed by her. Then he will be able to concern himself with her from the position of having himself.

Putting the struggle in the larger context of a lifelong struggle, first with his mother, and then with his wife, enables this man to focus on his search for individuality and autonomy and to see he is moving in that direction by his assertion with his wife.

A great deal of what happens in the revolution depends on the personal history. The patient who has had some experiences with being for himself in the past can trust the capacity of his basic biology. If he has not had that experience, as schizophrenics have not, he is launched into the unknown with little to go by.

But in addition to this difficulty, there is a feature of all rigid plans of behavior which is particularly harmful at this point: the demand for perfection, certainty, order, and precision. All uncertainty needs either to be denied or incorporated into the given system; an image of perfection attempts to guide the behavior. But in the revolution, the key experience is continual uncertainty.

CHAPTER 7

Revolution: Breakdown and Breakthrough

As we have seen, a rigid plan of behavior evolves out of a basic *fear* of vulnerability. At the core of an awareness of vulnerability are the early body experiences which are fragmented and confused. Maria Selvini-Palazzoli[1] has written an unusually perceptive paper on the importance of the body image of patients and especially of patients who suffer from anorexia nervosa. At one point, she observes:

From a genetic point of view, it appears that, from a very early age, the parents of these patients consistently force on their children their own personal and arbitrary interpretations of their children's bodily needs. The parental interpretations had but few connections with the patient's actual subjective experience. This produced confusion and mistrust in the patients toward their own primary source of experience—their own body. The feeling of identity, including bodily identity, seems to consist in an explicit and implicit self image that, in spite of the constant flux of internal and external stimuli, gives experience its continuity and consistency. Identity processes may be considered to be those ego functions through which the self is perceived to be differentiated from the non-self.

In other words, the basis for an open system, that is, one which responds to novelty, is a fundamental respect for body processes.

As Piaget and others have demonstrated, an infant develops a sense of self through his ongoing physical experience. In the early months, elements of his physical system are experienced in various combinations, and various forms of integrating occur. In the absence of the "normal" basic organizational exercise, rigid plans become necessary. When the revolution destroys these plans, it leaves the person *open* but with an old, unresolved fragmented body organization.

Many of the part-object forms that appear at this stage have a sexual cast: these sexual forms are manifestations of one possibility for integrating in the interpersonal mode. In effect, the patient is having body feelings for the first time and is looking for a way to conceptualize them. Thus, the numerous sexual associations at the beginning of a psychotic episode allow for concrete, skin-to-skin forming, just as the earliest forms of cognition through which the infant first found his place in the world were in attachment to his mother, skin-to-skin.

Patients also express anxiety through these sexual associations, but the anxiety is fundamentally about the awareness of separateness and body presence. The sexual aspect is the surface effort to integrate and make whole. The move to sexual associations is an attempt to "do away with" the separateness of self through a symbiotic merger with a therapist or other. It is worth noting that in our culture, it is more acceptable to express anxiety about wanting to have sexual relations with a therapist than it is to have the anxiety about feelings of separateness.

Searles[2] has interpreted the concrete thinking in psychotics as a defense which protects the patient and represses the anxiety-laden affects. This is perhaps a negative view of a very positive thrusting development in which the patient is moving to encounter himself in his feeling and knowing. Searles himself points out that with increasing ego differentiation there is an increasing capacity for symbolization and metaphoric thinking. Another way of putting it is that these patients are just becoming able to experience their own particulars, and to make patterns for the first time. They are coming to see the universal and repetitive in the concrete singular particulars of which they have become aware.

The anxiety of uncertainty may result in the externalization of new segments of organization. The necessity for externalization signals the inadequate state of the person's capacity to handle his new positive thrust.

But with the appearance of part-object symbols, sexual or otherwise, we can say that a whole and complete organization has now become a possibility for the future, since there is present evidence of at least partial integration. Usually the complete, part-object organization creates severe anxiety.

In effect, these patients are struggling to make sense in a world of chaos. They have become so involved in the moment by moment terror of concrete particulars that they are only reactions and reactors. As an analyst, I try to communicate to them that they are, in fact, in a purposive action. Sometimes, the patient can say, "Yes, I see I am feeling very anxious and am criticizing myself for being anxious," and move from the sense of doubt and shifting balance to working on the uncertainties he feels. It is like a disorganized and disgruntled country that suddenly finds a leader to organize the capacities of the populace for work toward a common goal. The patient is able to search himself, explore his presence, and feel into the uncertainty without being besieged by the feeling that he is bad because he is doubting. I try to help him see he is bigger than what is happening to him at the moment. Realizing this fact is frequently an organizing event.

But if the patient is unable to tolerate the anxiety and develops a directive effort during the revolution, there may be a reorganization around the previous values. This may then leave a segmentalization of some of the new organizing processes. They are foreign bodies which have formed and develop in an atmosphere which does not support them, though the therapist may be alert to their larval presence. These part-forms stimulate severe anxiety. This may result in the expression of aberrant forms such as somatic symptoms, bizarre ideation, or unusual images. Each of these externalizations of new segments of organization manifests the conflict between the new and the old organizations.

HALLUCINATIONS

Among the most dramatic forms of externalization are the hallucinations of the person in a psychotic process. One current definition[3] of hallucination is:

disorders of perceptual experience in which ideas and the images associated with them become so vivid that the experiencer insists on the truth of his experience despite sensory evidence to the contrary and despite anyone's remonstrances to the effect that his sensory experiences are false.

This definition emphasizes the aspects of disorder. But we can also see that hallucinations are ways of ordering. They are the part-forms of the incipient process which are reacting with the old forms of organization. They are attempts to unite the various directions of the various subsystems. Lang,[4] who has experienced psychosis, has written extensively on hallucinations. He writes:

Because of the subjective factors present in the experience of hallucinations, the patient obviously finds difficulty in considering them objectively and in reporting them with any degree of objectivity. Yet the report of the psychotic patient provides the basic data concerning hallucination phenomena . . .

As a schizophrenic who, though he has experienced various types of hallucinations over a period of more than eight years, has still retained a certain amount of intelligence, and who has some knowledge of general psychiatric literature, the writer feels that an account of the phenomena which he has experienced might be of some value. While he makes no pretense he has completely eliminated subjective factors, he has attempted to be as objective as the circumstances would permit . . .

If there is anything that I can say with certainty concerning the problems of hallucinations, it is that hallucinations are not the product of the activity of the conscious self, of the experiencing individual. The conscious self acts merely as a spectator. It does not anticipate; it does not initiate; it does not control the hallucinations. To the conscious self, hallucinations come as phenomena which it experiences. They reach it as already organized configurations. They are, to the self, phenomena which arise outside its range.

By conscious self, Lang means the old plans of behavior. The rigid plan still governs the total system, and the appearance of new possibilities for direction creates a conflict. He writes further:

The problem of hallucinations looms as an important one for the understanding of the nature of psychopathological conditions. From the viewpoint of actual experience, hallucinations form the epicenter from which the psychosis spreads. The clarification of the hallucinatory process will lead far toward the understanding of psychopathology. The complexity of the patterns of the hallucination suggests the existence of some form of organizing factor.

This hallucinatory situation is an attempt to organize new and important processes, especially when they involve certain kinds of frightening experience. Thus, the presence of the hallucinations reveals a freedom from the static nature of the rigid plans. The psychotic hallucinator is engaged in an active, thrusting move to develop and the use of drugs, at this stage, while often necessary, must be seen for its damaging effects.

In this regard, it is of particular interest to consider a statement by Freud[5]:

> . . . the problem of psychoses would be simple and intelligible if the withdrawal of the ego from reality could be carried through completely. But that seems rarely if ever to happen. Even so far removed from the reality of the external world as hallucinatory confusional states, one learns . . . that at the time in some corner of their mind, there was a normal person hidden, who watched the hubbub of the illness go past, like a disinterested spectator . . . What occurs in all such cases is a split in the mind. Two mental attitudes have been formed instead of a single one–one, the normal one, which takes account of reality, and another which under the influence of the instincts detaches the ego from reality.

The psychotic process involves more of the "person" than it does of "aberrance". Freud recognized there was more than the one form. The person who is psychotic is in fact quite alienated and disturbed *prior* to the onset of this manifest form–the psychosis. He never was "normal". The processes of the psychosis are looked upon with irony by the alienated, formed, rigid (supposedly "normal" [Freud]) schizophrenic part of the personality. The "normal" that Freud sees as looking, somewhat benevolently, on the "crazy", is, in fact, the old self watching the new part of the being that is moving away from the old schizophrenic form.

Larry begins to feel his wife is sending poison gas under the door. He has concretized the feeling that she is poisoning his life. But, in fact, the feeling that she is ruining his life can be traced to the new awareness he has of her. He has begun to like her and to feel that she is a person in her own right to whom he can talk and relate. However, in the discovery of all these new feelings, he finds many uncertainties such as how she reminds him of his mother, the fear he has of being overwhelmed by his liking of her, and his fear of his dependency on her. In sum, his wife is challenging his pride system which rules that he should never feel anxious and should never feel uncertainty and conflict. In this way, he has come to feel his wife is poisoning his life (i.e., his pride). But this sense of being poisoned is unacceptable as well, since he is not supposed to have hostile feelings toward anyone; hostile feelings indicate an imperfection and uncertainty. Thus, he concretizes and externalizes all this in the form of his delusion of poison gas. This delusion serves primarily to organize his new feelings about his wife. Freud would have viewed Larry's delusion as a withdrawal from reality. Actually, we can see these delusions are his first attempts at *contacting* reality.

THE BODY AS THE ARENA OF CHANGE

Pain, terror, awareness of processes which are not organized, hallucinations, somatic discomfort, and weird uncanny feelings that the world is falling apart–these appear as the patient begins to shift his direction of being.

For the first time, Rachel said "no" to a request of her father to come and take care of him while her mother went on a trip. Ordinarily, Rachel would have said "yes" automatically and continued in a structure in which she felt she was making up to her father for what the mother had not given him, and in which she was intimately involved in pitying herself for her sacrifice. Saying no was, in a very real sense, a revolutionary commitment to being alone in her own separate forming. She experienced when she said "no" to him a simultaneous "yes" to herself, a "yes" to being on her own. But the act was followed by total body immobilization, aches, pains, and weakness which required confinement to bed for twenty-four hours. Rachel had felt the experience of beginning to organize her own processes to be an overwhelming event. Eventually she decided to consolidate a relationship with a man of her own age who was as demanding as the father. A painter, she could not choose to work for herself but abdicated that arena to take care of this new man. Whether or not she will ever be able to stand up for her own creative capacities only time will tell.

WORLD DESTRUCTION DREAMS

Frequently patients begin to have world destruction dreams at the point where the old plan breaks down. This is because they have known only their commitment to a world of pretense and now, in the revolution, are left with disorganization and its attendant terror.

Over a ten-year period, Mrs. O had world destruction dreams whenever there was a shift toward looking at things on her own. Prior to each dream, she would experience disorganization, but also evidence of making choices which had some connection to her wants. Each time she was operating less in the form of the plans she had been following since childhood, plans which she had come to identify as "remaining at one with her mother". In the first dream, she felt herself running in panic as the enemy was about to blow up her city. Several years later, in another of these dreams, she was talking to her boyfriend who insisted that even though destruction was going on all around them, it was important for the nobility of mankind that they deliver the mail. In subsequent dreams, she turned to fight the destruction and formed coalitions with people whom she felt to be more in favor of her autonomy. Obviously, the progress of her relationship to the destruction in these dreams mirrored a shift in the forms of organization she employed in uncertainty. She was engaging the dilemmas and acting differently from her mother.

In his book, *Varieties of Psychopathological Experience* Carney Landis[6] asserts that two major considerations occupy a schizophrenic patient during the beginning period of psychosis. First, there is a realization of a loss of self-control, and, second, an attempt, usually *unsuccessful*, to explain this to himself. Landis lists several circumstances seen at the psychotic onset: physical illness, fatigue, and exhaustion, pain and tension, and fear. Each of these expresses a primary experience in the pre-rationative symbolism of body language. The previous schizophrenic situation was a state of being more or less disconnected from self; now these symbolizings in the form of pains, tensions, and physical integrations convey a coming-into-being. Immediately, the sense of loss of control supervenes.

David Shakow[7] observes that the acute schizophrenic patient often feels he is in a forest and has

> [a] multitude of thrilling new experiences, reacting high affectively, for instance to novel and unusual patterns of light on the leaves, or to unusual and subtle patterns of form in the branches. These are presumably expressions of the perceptive-associative processes which among normal persons, even when they are activated, are held under central control. In acute psychotic conditions, however, they are permitted to take over.

The new experience is found by some psychotics to be quite pleasurable, by others quite frightening. The latter will experience the psychotic state as pain, tensioning, or illness. The very newness of real experiencing naturally makes control difficult and more experience is needed before sufficient organization can occur.

One of Bleuler's[8] cardinal symptoms of schizophrenia is blunting of affect. The processes seen here represent an *affect activity*. This is confirmed by the fact that acutely psychotic patients suffer fewer ill-effects from dream and sleep deprivation than do other patients. Apparently, they are actively processing their realities during conscious life.[9]

One of Vailliant's[10] criteria for a good prognosis in acute psychosis is clear evidence of an *affective* psychosis. In other types of patients, we have seen that the active connection with the dilemmas leads to integration. So Vailliant's finding is consistent. Rubins[11] reports on his patient's gradual decrease in somatic symptoms with the recognition of and participation in conflict. Martin[12] has written about the importance of body participation in conflict and Kelman[13] has noted the curative effects of involvement in body process. The evidence is clear that as patients become more involved in forming and connecting to their own feelings, part-object symbolizing and integrating in forms of body involvement decrease. The patients show fewer wide swings of anxiety and are more able to live with tension.

As the revolution unfolds, the patient begins to realize the importance of his own perceptions in knowing the world. He experiences the importance of his personal vision, hearing, touching, smelling. Nostalgically, he may reminisce that his alienation has been a denying of these processes. He sees with growing clarity that he had been depending on the objectifications of others to the exclusion of his own subjectivity. His subjectivity, thus, becomes of primary importance.

Judge Schreber says[13]:

> I wish to add another point in connection with God's inability to understand the living human being as an organism and to judge his thinking correctly, which has been in many ways important to me. I can put this point briefly: *everything that*

happens is in reference to me. Writing this sentence I am fully aware that other people may be tempted to think that I am pathologically conceited; I know very well that this tendency to relate to everything that happens into connection with one's own person, is a common phenomenon about mental patients. But in my case the very reverse obtains. Since God entered into nerve-contact with me exclusively, I became in a way for God the only human being, or simply the human being around whom everything turns, to whom everything that happens must be related, and who therefore, from his own point of view, must also relate all things to himself.

We make a mistake if we look at this statement only literally and do not consider it as an attempt to express a struggle. First, Schreber is beginning to realize the importance of his *being-in-experience*. He talks of being the center of the world, which, in one sense, he is: what he *feels* is important; it is everything that he knows and perceives in the world. God he says (as a symbol for Nature), has entered into nerve contact; in other words, he is beginning to allow himself to feel, with his own sense organs, what exists in the world. Alfred North Whitehead,[14] the eminent philosopher, wrote:

If you try to imagine this doctrine in terms of our conventional views of space and time, which presuppose simple location, it is a great paradox. But if you think of it in terms of our naive experience, it is a mere transcript of the obvious facts. You are in a certain place perceiving things. Your perceptions take place where you are, and are entirely dependent on how your body is functioning. But this functioning of the body in one place, exhibits for your cognizance an aspect of the distant environment, fading away into the general knowledge that there are things beyond . . .

Whitehead also puts experience into center stage. He emphasizes logically that to which Schreber more anxiously and poetically attests: the person is the center of experience. But obviously Schreber lacks the assurance of Whitehead. Schreber is in the process of confronting considerable opposition in himself and the world (as he has known it), so he is alone in his assertion and is searching for words to express his feeling. Whitehead, on the other hand, educated in the language of philosophy and sensory psychology, has consensual maps and theories available to express his state of mind. Being someone with a capacity for organizing, Whitehead has available a hierarchy of levels in which to operate. Anything he does has many connections. He is clear about most of these. He sees his feelings and immediately connects them to other forms. As a result he is not alone in his feeling. Schreber, however, is still new, diffuse, and anxiously involved at *one* level. He does not integrate his perceptions with other features of his experience. He does not experience integrating and he lacks an organizing factor. He *is* alone.

FEAR

This sense of aloneness may soon develop into *fear*. Fear is an indicator that the person is an actively involved participant and is moving toward new forming.

A patient in this stage of the revolution may express the nature of his fear in language which is direct and to the point. Laing[15] quotes a patient as saying:

I didn't have the capacity for experiencing it. I experienced it for a moment or two but it was like a sudden blast of light, wind, or whatever you like to put it as, against you so that you feel you are too naked and alone to be able to withstand it, you're not strong enough.

Another man wrote[16]:

My fear was based fundamentally upon a terror of myself, of what was happening to me, of the helplessness which was overpowering my faculties, and it manifests itself first in a mounting fear of everything about me. I began to be afraid of people, of my family and my friends; not because of what they represent, I soon learned, but because of my own inability to cope with ordinary human contacts. The world which the others inhabited, to which I rightly belonged, was becoming unreal to me and I felt myself an alien as I trudged farther and farther into weird and unknown terrain.

One woman I worked with reported that she stood paralyzed on the top of the ski slope, afraid to move because when she knew that when she went down, she would be afraid. She was afraid to be afraid. Her fear was a basic terror of being vulnerable and uncertain.

Fear in revolution is the patient's deeper awareness of the direction in which he is moving. He is beginning to realize that the new forms will confront him with real questions and necessities for involvement. His passive detachment is disrupted. One patient observed[17]:

It was New Year's Day when I first experienced what I call *FEAR*. It literally fell on me, how I know not . . . Suddenly fear–agonizing boundless fear, overcame me, not the usual uneasiness of unreality, but real fear such as one knows at the approach of danger, of calamity . . . I remained aware of the basis for the fear which from then on came over me at any moment of the day . . . During the earliest attacks of fear and intense unreality, I sometimes uttered these words: "I should prefer to escape into madness to avoid this consuming fear." Alas, I did not know what I was saying. In my ignorance I believed that madness was a state of insensibility and not responsibility. Never had I imagined what "to lose one's reason" actually meant . . .

Or another:

Do you realize when I leave you I will be so normal I won't be able to stand the world. I will commit suicide. Do you realize you are destroying me?

This last patient, an adolescent, had been feeling the inconsistencies in his parents and friends. He had begun to sense their duplicity and his own duplicity in being with them. He noted how tense his father became whenever involved in any new experience. He felt he could not respect such a terrified man. A young man, age 17, he had, for weeks, been railing against the middle class mores of all those around. He was growing more intolerant of his own rigidity, though still afraid of exploring his own spontaneous behavior. When he did venture out on his own, he became fearful of separation from the only structures he knew.

In borderline or schizophrenic patients, we may see that fear in this stage of revolution brings different results. The schizophrenic's sense of possibility in new forms is vague. There may be little or no capacity for facing the difficulties with the revolution. Fear and anxiety can produce something like the experience recounted by Hannah Green in *I Never Promised You a Rose Garden.*[18]

"Oh, Miss Blau . . . " a voice called behind her. It was one of the social workers (what now? she wondered. I have a room, so I don't need a room tracker unless there's one to rescind the other's trackings.) Doctor Oster was talking to me about you going to the high school. (There it was again the lock-step-lock of the world; they had reassigned her to her place under the juggernaut.) Redness seethed upward from the tumor until she was hot to the eyes with pain.

In this case, Deborah, Hannah Green's character, had already moved out on her own, and was vaguely feeling herself to be a person when the old system, in the form of the social worker, began to classify her. To Deborah's sensitive ears, they had been talking about her as someone-who-could-not-function-on-her-own. According to that classification, she was someone who needed-constant-help-in-processing-reality; therefore, as was the case in her family system, she must believe her feelings and her responses were not right. Before this event, she was afraid, but was still trying to take care of herself. Those words of the social worker confirmed her fear about moving out on her own. Immediately, this whole process precipitated a conflict, strengthened her doubt of herself, and she was catapulted into anxiety; this was followed by anger (concretized as the tumor pain) and her total body disintegration:

The pain in the red wash was fading, but the panic was not withdrawing from her. *Listen to your heart* Anterrabae said, falling beside, she heard as if slamming like a latchless door in the wind. *"What is it? What is it?"* she called to Yr. *I was real, just here, just before.* Her vision was ragged and distorted and words came in an odd form, as if even Yri had been coded for secrecy. *Why? Why is this happening?*

Anterrabae is Deborah's secret name for all the processes which are organized in a form "outside of herself". That is, those processes by which she acclimatized herself to what was demanded of her by her mother's needs and her own need to be independent. Anterrabae tells Deborah that she is frightened and anxious about her separateness, that she is in danger and that she should retreat from this alive contact with her intentions.

It is at such moments in the revolution that many therapists fail their patients, for they take the fright to be an indication that the patient need not, and should not, go on. But, in fact, fear is a positive sign of processing information. The appearance of fear and anxiety are evidence that the individual has moved into an unfavorable direction from the view of the old organization. In attempting to assuage the pain, the psychiatrist or helper becomes like the mother who, seeing the child stumble when he runs to chase a pigeon, says "There, I told you you should never leave your mother."

BARRIERS TO THE REVOLUTION

As he stands alone in the revolution, the patient is faced with all kinds of doubt about his usefulness and productivity. This is understandable as we consider the magnitude of the forces which are being brought to bear against him. He is entering a world in which, as far as he can see, he is the only human.

> I went into a state which gave me cause for doubt. I moved as though in a dream. All the fairy stories and romances I have read seemed to come alive.[19]

To stand alone is difficult for the strongest of us; for the schizophrenic, it is a thousand times harder. But perhaps the greatest difficulty is that it is at this stage that the schizophrenic or profoundly revolutionized patient frequently comes in contact with a hospital and/or other representative of society's establishment.

As we have discussed, the use of autonomous feelings is classified as inhuman by the parental myths. In this designation, the old plan receives assistance from the establishment's representatives, the mental hospital and institutional departments of psychiatry. As others have observed, the thinking in these departments and in the hospital is basically ultrasympathetic to the family's diagnoses of the situation and the needs of the community. Increasingly financed by the Federal Government, these institutions are rapidly losing what little connection and feeling for the individual they ever had. The institutionalized versions of therapeusis are more and more coming to represent the needs of the family, which are to point out to the disturbed or psychotic person, that he is in the wrong (even if they claim it's "not his fault"). The reasons for this are perhaps cultural.

The going principle or tone of today's society amounts to an idolatry for speed, smoothness, and efficiency. (These are symbolized by computers and mechanizations.) Such ideas permeate the air. And we must add to this the enormous passivity expressed by a people who spend hours upon hours in front of television sets watching other people live and feel for them.*

The psychotic person in the gradually developing, slow, and painful revolutionary process is in direct conflict with the values behind such a culture and the

---

*The conflicts of adolescents can be attributed to a biologically new and hesitant stage of development. It is a gradual evolving attempt on the part of the individual to find a meaningful sense of values for the self. The technological world values closure and the smoothly functioning machine, and does not tolerate the necessary struggle of evolving organic process.

institutions and organized society of psychiatry; this is typified by the continual and increasing use of tranquillizers, electric shock and community psychiatry modalities which do not allow for the kind of processes important to self-realization. Obviously, there are places for these modes of treatment. But it is clear that they are currently primarily outgrowths of an establishment which needs to quiet the patient and prevent him from knowing that he has stumbled on to a new fact. They serve to block his awareness that he is in a position for real confrontation and development. Instead, they offer the oblivion of non-being: in tranquillizers and/or return to a community which the patient may not want, or be ready to meet.

In addition, psychiatry continues to sustain the notion that the person involved in the psychotic process or other form of disorganization, is altered or infested by a disease, a virus, or some abnormal chemical. This leads to the continual searching for a particular cause with the fantasy that all will be explained once that cause is found. The patient is thus given a label signifying that he is infested, that he is the sick, so no concern with the dynamic personal process is raised. This kind of thinking can be compared to that involved in the thesis which contends that man is basically hostile. Through this thesis, one attempts to abdicate his *responsibility* for determining the *dynamics* of hostility.

David Cooper,[20] British psychoanalyst and collaborator with Laing, has written:

> In concrete fact, there is very little explicit awareness about what really happens when someone goes into a mental hospital ward. Not only does the patient's physical bed await him in the ward, but there is also a procrustean bed of staff preconceptions into which he must be fitted at whatever cost in terms of mutilation of his personal reality. The violence that commences in his family is perpetuated in the conventional psychiatric ward. Most apparent psychiatric progress expressed in the catchwords "open doors", "permissiveness", "informality", "friendly staff-patient relations", serves to obscure this far more central area in which the traditional psychiatric hospital has not advanced since the days of Kraeplin in the last century.

The patient caught in the problems of his evolving uncertainty enters the hospital, and, as Cooper says, is fitted into preconceptions labelling him as sick and wrong. Cooper also points to the epidemic of pseudo-intimacy which is the current vogue in the psychiatric hospitals. As he observes, this clouds the issue even further. In the throes of a life and death struggle, psychotics, who have long known the dangers in interpersonal relations and have seen the deceptions to which they are prone, are now subjected to more of the same. In the hospital they are confronted with the same hypocrisy and are faced with understanding it in an arena that boasts its therapeutic virtues. It is the family all over again, or worse.

In cultures where the experience of personal disorganization is respected, we can see an entirely different approach to the revolutionized person. The individual who suddenly loses himself and withdraws from society into a frenzy of aberrant acts is not labelled diseased; on the contrary, he may even be idolized. Such culture groups as a whole recognize a hope and possibility in the aberrant situation. They make an effort to help understand the new world by calling on a shaman to "teach the spirits and how to summon and control them". In this process, they help identify rather than obscure the new fact. There is a deep respect for the unusual and for the fact that Nature has ways of healing which may be beyond the rationation of theories.[21,22]

But when a period of possibility arises for the revolutionized in our culture, there is no help; so it is understandable that these persons, forced into the terror of the unknown and unsupported by their society, will be pervaded by doubt.

CHAPTER 8

Depression: The Necessary Transition

When patients get involved in doubts, it is essential for a therapist to move very gently. He must do so, however, with a full awareness that the next event is often a full blown, unavoidable, possibly very serious depression. As one patient wrote:

> That night, the creeping tide of depression washed away the sand of self esteem. I was a fool to think I could win. There was no victory for such as me. I was a crippled puppy running by the road, dust on a cathedral floor, a blind lion, for me there was no hope. Was there anyone at all? There was no one at all. My wife had betrayed me to my enemies. I was separated from my family, afraid of my children. I looked about the room in which I lay . . . I was thinking of the insane . . . I was the giant of cardboard and this was my jail. All was depression. Days during which it was very night, sleepless nights unending, and I did what they told me . . . I was silent . . . others made jewelry or wallets, I made nothing . . . It was as if they had been there forever . . . just the setting for my own struggle. The depression was with me and the terrible feelings of being caught. It was not the feeling of being caught that comes when you are tired of running and hiding and questioning; it is the feeling of being caught that comes first time that you are caught.[1]

This man is both lost and caught; his momentum in the process has "grabbed him" and he is going in it. His images are his effort to organize the meaning of the process. He feels crippled, which is his deeper awareness of how maimed and hurt he has been throughout his life, as well as his sense of inadequacy in his struggle. He talks of being a king in separation from his kingdom, perhaps an indication that he knows he could have had a more personal and integral life than he has had. At this point, he is between the old and the new and his depression represents the point of transition.

Patients experience this depression as deadness and a feeling that they are cut off. In effect, they *are* cut off–cut off from all they have known in their world.

One woman wrote[2]:

> For ten days, the dry beach. My scalp strained as if some nerve would break at any moment, but the interior of my head felt empty and ugly as if its cells had been hollowed out by a ruthless knife replaced with a sandy sphere. The spider had scalloped it out, I recalled then I remembered that the operators had been delusions.

Winnicott[3] calls this period "a regression to the real self": the breakdown from which forms may emerge.

One woman I treated started saying how depressed she felt. She could not understand it, but it was a sense that she could not get into herself. Her depression occurred subsequent to a deep involvement in a conflict about asking her boss for a raise. She felt she could not take the risk and responsibilities that went with the higher salary. When she did finally break through the structure of not asking, she felt cut off from the symbiotic position of being a sinecure. She was, she said, cast into "the limelight" with the very authority she both "wanted and feared".

Many investigators have remarked that with schizophrenic patients, depression follows acute psychosis. Eissler[4] has called this the "phase of relative clinical muteness". He found it to be central, claiming "the whole question of psychoanalysis of schizophrenia can be decided only in [this] phase". This is the period when the patient must begin to consolidate his new experiences.

Bowers[5] notes that the depression may be marked by long, painful silences, resistances, and apathy; feelings of worthlessness and guilt, the vegetative signs of weight loss, anorexia, or constipation. It may appear unexpectedly after a flamboyant active psychotic period during which some may be deceived into believing the patient has been cured. Faberow reports that in thirty schizophrenic patients who committed suicide, almost all cases occurred after there was a remission of illness; that is, after the anxiety of the initial conflict.[6] Depression is a necessary experience for anyone who must realize that he is letting go of an old mode of being and moving on to a new path. Many people, however, need help in resolving the conflict.

Another of Vailliant's criteria[7] for predicting recovery from schizophrenia is a "concern with death". This is connected with the patient's process when he begins to take his life seriously and moves from a pride-imagination-guided-system into reality. Every person at this point comes to face one basic fact: his own being-as-termination. The concern with death is a sign of the depression stage. The patient has given up the narcissistic position of being merged in the family plan and is directed toward realizing his separateness. Roth states[6]:

> I suggest that these are affects that are experienced in the process of responding to loss, and the greater the ability of the psychotic ego to respond to loss, the greater the likelihood it will move toward health.

Mourning is not only a concern with the loss of the old identity; it is part of accepting the responsibility for a new life. Roth reports that he says to his patients:

> Can you bear the pain of your sadness? As bitter as it sounds, we can view this as a good sign you are now depressed over what formerly drove you crazy. Let's examine it together and see what it was you couldn't bear.

It is of more than passing interest that two other investigators, Sonnenberg and Miller,[8] feel that the depression phase does not occur in patients who are put on large psychiatric wards and do not receive attention from any one single person. This suggests that patients who do not get personal help shift back into the old rigid plan of behavior. This is true especially of patients who have been given drugs which attenuate the depression processes. It also suggests that the connection with "one person" can make it possible for the individual to move into the *new world*. We know from years of psychotherapeutic research, that when this other is attentive to the patient's needs, there is a gradual opening into the disorganization.

* * *

Thus the depression phase follows upon the realization that living in a detached or alienated form is inadequate. There is always an essential poignancy to these moments when the patient reverberates with the emotions of knowing how and to what extent he has been bypassing the intimacy of his own second by second living in the world. The pain of this depression catapults him into the dilemma of a stage I call the "immersion". Here, implicitly, he must begin to make distinctions among the nuances of his feelings, to tease apart the difference between what he wants and what others want from him. He must do all this or continue to feel, as one patient put it, like an "atom bomb has just gone off in him" and "is continuing to emit small explosions every minute". It is only some sort of autonomous organization of self which can still this disturbance. And this organization must emerge organically out of the struggle with ambiguities rather than being imposed.

In fact, flashing awareness of the immersion in the reality of forming leads, in effect, to a fork in the road toward the autonomous self. At this fork, patients either choose to take up the challenge by moving into the process of differentiating, focussing, and conflict, or they consolidate into new but still essentially rigid forms, such as paranoia, forms in which they attempt to avoid the continuing confrontation with immersion. The two paths that constitute this fork will be discussed in the following chapters.

Part IV

THE “EXPERIENCE OF LIVING” PROCESS

CHAPTER 9

Immersion and the Path of Retreat

Ordinarily, when a person lets go of a cognitive form, he breaks through a set which has blocked his appreciation of relating. In the revolution and depression, he perceives how he has been following the old plans which have denied his ongoing presence and, as this experience deepens, he begins to explore his capacities and to immerse himself in his own forming process. Immersion involves the patient in the awareness that there is something behind the forms and objects of his life. He begins to feel the manifold ways his feeling affects how and what he sees; he begins also to sense the extent to which at every moment he is a changing, flowing process; he begins to see the forms and models he makes; how other people are, how he is, and how his relationships flow immediately from his tensions.

In the early stage of immersion, the patient may seem rather indirect and vague. He may even have a slightly clouded consciousness with a very wide range of vision, a paradox in itself. He may focus on sensations and shifts in body tensions. He may talk about the ineffable aspect of his experience and emphasize that it is impossible for him to be specific because he sees that any attempt to delineate one aspect falsifies it because everything flows into and makes connections with everything else. In all this, he may convey what appears to be intense egocentricity. But it is only a relative egocentricity because he is in the process of making connections to the outside world on the basis of his experience.

In the immersion process, many strange images, fantasies, and experiences may arise. There may be out-of-body events in which the patient feels himself leaving his own physical position and "taking a look at himself" from the outside. He may feel his self go somewhere else, leaving the physical presence behind. He may experience himself as broken in fragments with his body parts in different places in the room or even in different locations in the world. He may begin to feel the flow of images intensely and be unable to stop focusing on them; he may see new, strange, bizarre events, present, past, and future, images which contain condensations of his current experience of himself, whether as an outstanding figure or as a depreciated worm. He may experience the flow of making forms with these images and begin to be able to transform some of his terror of the unknown by actively working to change the images in his own consciousness. Or nothing may come together: it may all remain fragmented, as with one patient of mine who kept dreaming of digging up his body parts and never being able to put himself together.

Each of these varieties of experience in the immersion represents the patient coming into flow of uncertainty. No matter how he "becomes" during this process, he must first experience the variety, the terror, the blocks, and the creative transformations. More often than not, immersion first leads to intense anxiety which results in a retreat into old shaping or into some new but limited form.

JOANNE

Joanne began to question her rigid form: *she-felt-she-had-to-be-a-perfect-mother*. This was a metaphor for controlling herself. The discussion around the concrete aspect of her need to be a perfect mother opened up the structure of how she limited herself in her relationship to her particular forming. When she let go of this structure, Joanne said, "This means I can take my children to the park only two times a day if I want to; I will not have to be taking them in order to be a good mother." It was obvious Joanne was still concerned with rigid forms: the number two, the necessity of the park, thinking in terms of the children while in a discussion of herself. But as she experienced more of the flow of her feeling, her discovery of her desire not to talk to the children every moment they wanted her, led her to anxiety over expressing her feelings and an awareness that she had to have her children with her to "devour them" because she did not want to be alone. (She filled her time with her concerns about her husband, son, and daughter.) This awareness emerged one day through a slip of the tongue while she was talking to her son. At his request that they take a taxi home from her work, where he had come to visit her, she said: "What, do you think you are married to a millionaire?"

On first coming to analysis, Joanne had been in terror that she might discover things about herself which she could not handle. When she heard this slip, she began to cry. She could not bear to see herself as the devouring, seductive mother; she was anxious and disrupted from her usual calm. At that moment, there was no way for her to actually organize the complexities of her feeling toward her son as a substitute for her husband, since this would lead to an awareness of her rage at her husband as a symbol for her father, for whom she had much unassimilated hate for his not taking care of her. The agony she went through over her (as she expressed it) imperfection was quite amazing; it was as if she had suddenly found herself disgusting and horrible. It became clear, as she talked, that this was because she had suddenly seen her feelings did not fit her plan to be a perfect mother. Her appreciation of this feeling toward her son opened her to experiences she had never lived: she became more sensitive to the nuances and variety of feeling in other aspects of her life. After the event with her son, she began to exercise her capacities to deal with her negative feelings toward her daughter, about whom she said:

I realized as I was talking to Laura on the phone, I did not want to talk to her and I did not want to see her. I felt like the most horrible person in the world when I hung up the phone and I cried and cried. After, however, I felt better. I realize now you have to go through the bad feelings to come to the good. When I arrived home from work I was surprised I felt quite delighted when I saw Laura and wanted to sit down and talk to her.

Not too long after, in a session, Joanne indicated that she was worried about how she would operate in this new openness; the old forms appeared again. She said she had difficulty understanding why a friend did not call her when the friend's father died. As Joanne saw it, friends *should* do that, and the friend's not doing it was threatening. As we discussed this, it became clear Joanne was needing the friend to act as she did because "having a friend" was something she did compulsively in order to protect herself from her own feelings. She could not contain her feelings of anxiety when alone and ran to tell her friends everything that happened in her life. In this case, she felt her friend had thrown her back on herself. It jeopardized the structure "everybody was friendly" with her. For a period after this immersion, she again felt more open to nuances of inner and outer life. This meant all the old positions had different angles of perception for her. Her new view of herself meant she was in a different position in her being in reality. She now had to look at things from a different perspective. She felt outside her boundaries. Her solution was to retreat back into the boundaries of her image as a "perfect mother".

EGO BOUNDARY: THE RIGID PLAN

The question of boundary formation is a confusing one. Often analysts think of boundaries as a kind of limit which allows the patient to keep out what he does not want and to let in what he does. Federn[1] has written about this:

> I would like to discuss here an observation often made about the term "ego boundary". A highly esteemed discussant of this theory refused to accept the idea that the ego has a distinct boundary because he felt that this term would indicate a strict linear, ribbon like, or ditchlike circumference of a territory. It seems to me that this discussant is not quite free of a static conception of the mental processes. His substitute ego periphery for ego boundary may be a good one; however, neither designation implies either a zone or a line of demarcation around the ego. Such a demarcation would be contrary to the nature of the ego itself as a changing union of components which are entering or leaving. The use of the words "boundary" or "periphery" is necessary to express the fact that the ego is actually felt to extend as far as the feeling of the unity of the ego contents reaches. This feeling sharply distinguishes everything that belongs to the ego in an actual moment of life from all the other mental elements and complexes not actually included in the ego. Because the feeling of a unit exists, there is also a boundary or limit of the unit.

But the use of such spatial terms as "extend" or "periphery" unwittingly supports the notion of a personality which is separate from connection in reality. The terms convey the very static conception of human functioning which Federn claims he is opposing. Phrases like "sharply distinguishes everything that belongs to the ego" indicate that what Federn and others call "ego boundaries" are actually the rigid plans: Joanne bounded her ego by the feeling of being a loving mother. When her engagement in reality extended beyond that functional shape into the feeling she was a devouring mother, she felt her boundaries were dissolved.

Perhaps a less confusing description of the phenomenon that has been described as ego boundary might be what we have been calling the "capacity to engage". This concept has the advantage of elucidating the holistic nature of the organism. It points up that the form of the organism is a certain shape of behavior and is itself a function of what the person can and cannot integrate. Those aspects of self-in-process which are excluded by the personality organization are present in their effect on the form. They are represented by the limits of the capacity to engage and by the inhibitions they force on the system. This concept of "capacity to engage" suggests a more dynamic and total conception of the process which considers the state of the organism as the making of connections and integrations to certain levels of complexity. Some interesting research data supports this idea:

A study by Louis Breger[2] and his colleagues involved subjects who underwent an intensive group therapy experience. After the group process in which one of the subjects was "put on the carpet", Breger and his colleagues studied the stressed individual's dreams in the laboratory. They found that those subjects who could engage the stress, that is, those that were not overly anxious, had dreams which showed evidence of active symbolic transformation processes. But some were overwhelmed, could not handle their experience, and could not make connection to it. This last group "had the greatest number of dreams containing *direct, stress-related* incorporation with relatively fewer symbolic transformations". They concretely pictured the stress in direct photographic-like illustrations. Similarly, it has been shown in other studies[3] that depressed patients tend to have "happy" dreams until they begin an "improvement". They begin to have depressed dreams when they are beginning to be able to confront and integrate their state of experiencing. Both sets of data demonstrate that the capacity to engage and transform the uncertainties of any experiencing process (stress and depression) indicates the extent of the individual's so called "ego boundaries".

In any personal revolution, false boundaries start dissolving as the actual capacity to engage becomes clear. Rennert[4] has observed that the position of the horizon in drawings of acute psychotics rises. The more severe the episode, the higher the line goes until it may disappear altogether leaving a maplike flatness which lacks perspective. Billig[5] has observed similar changes. This suggests the loss of falsely structured notions of up and down (distance and nearness), the presence of diffuse experience, and the inability to make differentiations. The loss of false boundaries may produce a terror because the patient's life with the false boundaries had been a compromise around the avoidance of facing incapacity. They anticipate similar experiences when more of their false boundaries collapse. Hannah Green[6] reports:

> Furii had told her that sanity had to do with challenge and choice, but challenge as Deborah knew it was the shock challenge that Yr created for her in snakes dropping from the walls, people and places disappearing, an awful jolt of collision of worlds.

The task of the patient in revolution is to proceed into and through these experiences of incapacity rather than backing away into psychotic distortions.

One night while working in a hospital, Oscar inadvertently aroused the hostility of a psychotic patient. The patient waited for him after he was off-duty and attempted to start a fight in the street. Oscar escaped unscathed, but terrorized. He was sure it would happen again. He kept reiterating his fear that he would be hurt, although he realized that this patient was really not so tough as he made out. Oscar kept wondering when the patient would pull a knife on him.

The terror Oscar experienced expressed his realistic fears; they also represented the fears he felt whenever he moved out of his false boundary into his true capacity to engage. When he released his grip on his obsessive forms, he experienced his terror. During the course of our five years together, Oscar had on six other occasions come to similar moments of immersion. Each time, he associated to a fear of being disorganized. As an adolescent, he had a friend and classmate who had been put in a mental hospital; he had another friend he liked during high school who had committed suicide; his grandmother had been hospitalized for psychotic behavior; and he himself had been depressed and quite disassociated during his adolescence. He associated to these aspects of his history whenever he experienced a moment of true participation.

We can observe that any two-week-old infant moves up against the edge of his crib. He would seem to be "searching for boundaries", a feeling of comfort in being up against something with which he can "connect" and "feel" unified. (Not so very unlike the way adolescents in rebellion crave an oppositional position against which to test themselves.) If the parents immediately move the infant away with a pseudo-rational explanation such as "you might suffocate", would the infant not then soon come to feel "what I do because of some basic unknown feeling is *not* all right; I'll have to look to see what is right from what they do to me." Or, what happens if the mother puts the child at the edge of the crib from the start–being a so-called "good mother" and "doing for her child". Would this not deprive him of the experience of moving from experiment to acting and integrating with his own capacities?

The capacity for ordering is already quite strongly and inherently present in the two-week-old infant; it is evident in his establishment of feeding schedules, in sucking, and eye fixation. When the mother "does for" her child, she prevents his experiencing for himself. Instead of evolving a true boundary of self as the capacity to engage, the child develops false boundaries in his imitation and conformance to the expectations of others. The child is not initially fearful of his explorations of the openness of uncertainty, but he becomes fearful in his experience with his family. Once these fears have developed and have been avoided by the old plans and false ego boundaries, it becomes increasingly difficult for the individual to trust himself in the uncertainty of immersion.

Borderline patients in immersion question whether they can say "no" to the demands they feel being made on them. They generally have avoided engagement, feeling that they have to say "yes" so as not to have to deal with the issues that another person or events present to them. They have refused to engage the moment by saying "no" because that would establish a differentiation between them and the person they said "no" to. Their form of organization has been that of saying yes-in-order-to-not-create-a-point-of-reference of themselves. They "attempt" to remain in immersion, often even dulling their awareness to their existence in that state.

The obsessive person, on the other hand, has organized himself around a rigid group of categories (reference points) and needs help in being open to a non-categorizing process. For both, these moments of immersion in the reality of forming are, at first, pure diffusion and terror. And many retreat from this terror—which has been created by the dissolution of the false boundaries—by creating new false boundaries in the form of Paranoia.

THE PARANOID EGO BOUNDARY: TRANSFORMING THE IMMERSION ANXIETY

In the paranoid state of schizophrenia, the overwhelming arousal and uncertainty of the immersion must be faced and integrated by an organism which has only minimal capacity for transformation. There is, consequently, the emergence of an external, paranoid structure (boundary) for ordering because schizophrenics are "unable to organize and subordinate the events occurring simultaneously in their organisms".

Voth[7] has shown that if a normal individual sits in a dark room and looks at a small spot of stationary light, he will see it move. This is because, as we have noted, there is the continual movement of the eyeball of which we are usually unaware. In the dark, we become more aware of our own process and thus feel the stationary light as moving. Voth has found that paranoid individuals tend *not* to see the light moving. For them, it is stationary. In other words, they organize in the uncertainty by being non-responsive to their internal process because of the anxiety they feel. Apparently their immersion (a dark room) anxiety is so overwhelming, they are unable to proceed with even the simplest forms of integration.

The paranoid state represents something of a caricature of the process of linear boundary formation described by Federn. The paranoid is suspicious, rigid, tense, and especially willful. He has an intense fear of external control and feels anything may be a threat. He constantly searches for the meaning of events. He cannot ignore anything unusual. But when he is aware of particulars, he is unable to process them. In fact, his nervous system has become—because of the revolution—wide open to registering every event or phenomenon but is unable to order them except in the definitive point to point forms of projections or externalization.

Projections are "attributions to external figures of motivations, drives, or tensions that are repudiated and intolerable in oneself".[8] In other words, the paranoid is in a state of fear, of being overrun (controlled) by his own unmanageable processes. He is in immersion and is trying to protect himself from it.

After two years, Joe began to talk of his trust for me. He spoke for three quarters of one session about his feeling that I helped him. He mentioned many ways he was feeling better. We were immersed, to some degree, in an openness with each other. Then he *abruptly* shifted to talking of a fear that now while he lay exposed on the couch, I would take an ax and chop off his head.

Joe had always lived in a compulsive, rigid form. For example, he used *time* to force him to be at my office. He would do this by waiting until the last minute, until he could feel "pushed" to come. His father's demands that he succeed had been internalized and he used these to force him to live in the world rather than in bed. In the immersion, he became overwhelmed with the anxiety of having to create his being. He became afraid that he would "end up staying in bed all day". That is, he found himself without the artificial directives (Time and Success) and felt that if he stopped following these directives, he would have to live with his feeling about me, both hostile and affectionate, and would have to begin to discover what he was as a separate person in the novelty of our changing relationship from moment to moment. The symbolization that I was going to hit him with an ax prevented the open flow and organized him around a known, dangerous object to which he could relate directly.

The micro-transformations of a patient in paranoid forms are difficult to follow. Beginning therapists may not understand the tensional character of the paranoid form or its subtlety. Even advanced practitioners may not really appreciate the specific nature of the patient's anxiety about the open flow: the immediate terror of the immersion. These patients feel they are not able to manage what will happen, that any act will provoke an event which cannot be predicted, and, worse, that next event will involve them in a flow process which will lead to an interest and involvement. They complain that each action raises further questions about how a situation will evolve. They feel acutely a loss of control, a gut experience that the bottom is falling out, as a butterfly in the stomach, a weakness in the chest. Thus, the intimate intrapsychic moment is frequently transformed almost immediately and without awareness into a paranoid form. The question then becomes: "What will he do to me?" instead of "How do I feel?" The patient therefore gets further and further away from the basic terror of being in the immersion with himself. The following example demonstrates this process.

In one session, Henry came to the issue of trusting and having faith in me as his analyst. In our discussion, he said that he felt he could not trust me completely because he knew that even though he made mistakes, his clients liked him because he did them good and *not because he was infallible.* As he talked about this, he kept making a slip, saying he thought I was infallible when he meant to say he knew I was fallible, and the slip bothered him. Clearly, he needed me to be infallible. At this point, he "jumped" over to saying he did not think I should have charged him for a session which he had to cancel the previous month. He said he had called well ahead of the time we agreed was permissible if he was to avoid being charged. I pointed out to him that I *in fact* had *not* charged him for that session and I wondered why it was that he needed to have it that I did. Obviously, he had not read his bill correctly. He began to muse that it was clear to him he wanted to see me as "a *shit*" but he could not see why. In the next session, Henry discussed a dream he had that night. He noted that he has never been very athletic and could never perform very well in athletics. At the same time, all of his life he had been having terrific fantasies about what a great athlete he was. In his fantasies, he could shoot a basketball shot from half court and make it every time. He could hit homeruns and pitch perfect games in baseball every time he played. Though he cannot dive at all, in his fantasies, he could perform the "only sixty-three somersault dive" in the world. In Henry's dream he was "struck" by the fact that he was on Third Avenue "learning" (he emphasized the word) how to hit a ball. He did not know where the first pitch came from; he was not conscious of anyone throwing it but he hit it back on the ground. His seven-year-old son came up and asked what he was doing. He said, "I'm learning how to hit a ball." In the dream, he felt the swing, "I swung. This isn't good. I tried to *improve* my swing and I woke up finding it shocking, in a psychological sense." He felt it was particularly important he was doing this *learning* in front of his son, in fact giving his son *prima facie* evidence that his "old man was not a superstar".

As the vignette demonstrates, Henry's feelings of distrust were connected to his need for me (and himself) to be infallible. But at the same time, his distrust was an engagement at another, perhaps not-articulated-level, with his terror of the unknown. He had felt if one is fallible, it is "perfectly obvious" that it is not possible to be open to uncertainties. In essence, when he engaged his fallibility, the distrusting paranoia emerged (that I overcharged him) as an aspect of his re-establishing his need for control (*in*fallibility). He became at that moment grossly paranoid, cynical, and testy, someone who excluded learning; he became set against the fallibility that learning–i.e., not knowing, struggling, etc.–entails.

However, the living experience in the first reported session of his need for infallibility had made it possible for him to begin considering his fallibility, at least in a dream.

Sullivan[9] regards paranoia as a serious miscreation. While it does represent a miscreation, or rather, misdirecting of the thrust toward the autonomous self, the appearance of paranoia indicates that the schizophrenic has begun to appreciate the possibilities of utilizing his skills of organizing, but has not been able to continue because the immersion in novelty has become too threatening. Boisen writes:

> The [paranoid] reasoning process becomes the means by which the patient keeps his head above water. The ideas may be peculiar, but the speech coherent and the logic good enough, if only the premises could be accepted. Neither is there in such types any deficiency in affect.[10]

The paranoid—in contrast to other schizophrenic types—does not often distort his own personal "I", although he may omit it in favor of the name of someone he considers more definitive: a brother, a boss, a leader—figures of potency.[11] One patient I remember kept asking to see the President. When asked why he wanted to see the President, he said, "Because I know he will look after my rights."

Thus, paranoia indicates both the problem and the potential. Arieti[12] has cautioned that to help these people, analysts must encourage them to enlarge their attachment to internal objects. To put this in the terms we have been using here, analysts must help patients in the paranoid state connect with their forming and creating process.

RETREAT INTO BLOCKING PHENOMENA: INTELLECTUALIZING DEPENDENCIES, SEXUALIZING AND NARCOTIZING

The immersion dilemma may also lead into other forms of retreat besides paranoia, into forms of blocking: compulsive intellectualizing, for example, or, more commonly, various forms of dependency. Dependencies which appear in this stage of process are often subtle and difficult to identify.

One patient I treated began to fantasize that his mother was saying to him: "So you think you can have a meaningful life; you're kidding yourself; nothing will ever be any good for you." This association organized the patient's fears and connected to his feeling of hopelessness in the immersion disorganization. The dependency led to a temporary halt in the evolution of his autonomy. Another patient told me he heard his mother saying to him: "you don't have to suffer, it isn't worth it," something she had frequently told him when he was a child and an adolescent trying to develop. She had never wanted him to be separate and would offer him this fatal solace whenever he seemed to be moving in that direction. A third patient would enter the immersion anxiety feeling a sense of terror about his capacity to meet the challenge and would suddenly imagine that his wife had passed out somewhere and needed his help. As he later realized, he had felt his only power was his wife-mother and in his moment of immersion terror he felt his power inadequate to meet the challenge.

Sexuality may also become a block to immersion anxiety. Patients may involve themselves in elaborate fantasies, as did one patient of mine who ecstatically saw himself dissolved in masochistic sexual orgies with his girl friend or a prostitute he was going to pick up on the street; this fantasy circumvented his immediate feelings of terror about being with himself alone in the forming process.

Finally, blocking in the immersion may also appear in the form of drug or narcotic use. These chemical agents provide a secondary kind of disorganization which cannot be readily confronted and thus acts as an avoidance of confrontation. Patients who employ this mode of blocking may experience a blurred state of consciousness filled with multiple images and associations; they may feel open, but careful examination will inevitably reveal that this openness is really an experience broken in fragments with a marked absence of engagement in the forming process. Actual confrontation with forming involves experience of anxiety because of the need to face differences and similarities in oneself and others and the world.

* * *

Labeling and hospitalizing a patient who is struggling in the difficult state of immersion—whether in some form of blocking or in paranoia—has the effect of rejecting the very inner forming experience to which the patient must become deeply committed if he is to progress through immersion toward self-articulation. The doctor's labels serve to designate (and concretize) a person as an object, to establish a confrontation between the sane subject—the doctor—and the insane object, the patient. The locking of these positions may prevent any possibility of helping the patient integrate the immense uncertainties he must face.[13]

CHAPTER 10

Immersion and the Path of Making Distinctions

The person in immersion is confronted with a dilemma because if he does not retreat from the terror of forming into paranoia or if he can emerge from the stage of paranoia, he must begin the process of making distinctions; that is, he must begin to see and perceive the world as it is, without the old plan.

IMMERSION AND PERCEPTION

In order to understand this aspect of immersion, it is perhaps useful to think biologically. The type of people we have been discussing in this book have been described as "alienated". Specifically, this means that the kinds of experiences they have do not correlate with the ways they are feeling, thinking, and living them. To put it neurologically, the basic relationships in their nervous systems are not mirrored in the symbols and concepts they use to make meaning out of their environment.

Each of us is a sensitive registering of the perceptual differences that we "find" in reality. Our nervous system registers changes, in the form of alternating impulses between the nerves, responses of the nerves, patterns of the sets of nerves, and so on. These are relationships. We "make" them automatically into gestalts. It is this *automatic* gestalt-making function of the nervous system which leads to the sensation that we actually experience objects when, in fact, we are always living and being a process of *relating* to them. We are unaware of the rapid phase of active correlating by virtue of the structure of our nervous system. But when we feel growth or change, it is really a change in the relationships in our nervous systems, like the change experienced by getting a different view of a landscape, a different perspective. This is a difference in relationship which we register as new experience,[1] and which leads to different gestalts. But the initial aspect of change is in the relating process.

We make gestalts, then, by distinguishing the formal or common relationships among impulses. These relationships involve proportions of space and time which are mirrored in analogical models in the nervous system. We share these models with others who are having the same experience. Thus, the relationships can be said to mirror certain constancies in the world.

In the alienated person, the gestalts do not establish consistent connections to the perceptions. Instead, there is superimposition of a special, ad hoc, programmed organization which blocks out some perceptions and over-emphasizes others. There is usually an over-emphasis on those specific relationships which enable the person to hold his position in the family. In that case, the basic rule of an alienated system sets the system against considering or making any relationships (gestalts) other than the ones given by the family. In effect, this alienated program does not allow a person to develop an appreciation of the rules of transformation which connect his gestalts to his processes. He cannot form new gestalts flexibly. He cannot explore the relationships among his perceptions. He is unable to change his existing relationships. Therefore, when he leaves the family, he has a plan which makes him unable to live directly in reality processing; he attempts instead to employ certain formal relationships in dealing with his reality and must hope they apply. Whenever the feedback the alienated person gets from his perceptions runs counter to the plan he has for reality, he blocks out these discrepancies. But he does this at the cost of becoming a stranger to himself.

Scher[2] has compared the alienated state of being to that of a man living in a closed community where there are only two categories, intimate and stranger. In schizophrenia, according to Scher, intimacy and community exist only for the family; the rest of the world is viewed as hostile. But the alienation in schizophrenia and neurosis is from the self as well as from the world. The pseudo-intimacy of the intrapsychic closed community involves the family ideal and not the personal feeling of the self. The patients are connected to a gestalt–familial-denial-of-intimacy–and not with their own perceptions. Macnaab[3] has noticed schizophrenic alienation from existence, and other writers have noticed schizophrenics' alienation and separation from *all* relationships. All of these authors have focused on the predominant form, alienation, into which many of the schizophrenic's forming processes have consolidated. The revolution is an awakening of the discordance, and immersion is a *connection to perceiving*. And for some, especially schizophrenics, the process of clarifying the rules of perception must be learned from scratch.

Patients who become involved in the immersion stage will have a noticeable new sensitivity to discrepancies in their perceptions. They see there are real differences between the way they feel now and the way they have been making cognitive whole in the past. They become sensitive to these distinctions. As a result, there are *derealization* events in which patients become aware that previous thinking is not representative of their feeling.

Claire, for example, began to feel she was not in her body. She felt depersonalized. Prior to immersion, she had talked a great deal about her need for sex and her feeling about sexual needs, but she was un-connected to the feelings she had in our discussions. She was seeking sex as a mode of connecting to her body. She often commented on the emptiness she felt in her one-night-stand sexual contacts. She said she experienced herself as an automaton, not feeling anything, aware of her failure. On this occasion, I felt I could be most helpful by pointing out that this feeling of derealization was her first acknowledgment of the actual fact: it was true; she was literally *not* in her body; she was not connected with herself. Thus, in immersion, she had connected to her actuality—her lack of connections—and was feeling a beginning in a new form—self connection.

The patient may experience *déjà vu* events at this stage. The affectual contact within the immersion has led to an increase of total feeling experience. The patient, therefore, connects vague, undifferentiated aspects of different experiences because of the diffuseness of his level of general experience. As a result, the similarity of his feelings in many events is perceived. The sifting and compartmentalization of the distinction-making capacity which normally prevents the *déjà vu* in all of us must occur if the patient is to grow beyond *déjà vu* experiences.

Patients also begin, generally, to appreciate their surroundings. They will speak of a new ability to see color and dimensions. The world which had previously seemed to be no more than homogenized experience now begins to take on exciting aliveness. There is the recognition of distinctions in sizes of objects and/or they experience time in new ways. Patients begin to make significant contact with their hate and love for others. The more immersed they become, the more they come to see the similarities as well as the differences in the way they feel with, and about, other people. They come to realize that they are a complex network of relations. They speak of discovering that they are not the rigid categories they previously thought they were. And they discover they are related and relate to people in many different ways. They are aware of the similarities, for example, between the parts of one person and the parts of another. They recognize the unconscious messages that people send and they begin to feel their own subliminal perceptions.

Piaget[4] makes an interesting point about child development which is particularly helpful in understanding this process of making distinctions which occurs in the immersion. He notes that the development of concepts of "identity" occurs earlier than the development of the concept of "conservation". Identity is derived by "dissociating the permanent qualities from the variable qualities". By analogy, we have seen that an Idealized Image of Self is an organization built around a concept of self as *permanent*, rather than a concept of the self as a product of *spontaneity*.

According to Piaget, the child in his early years, before conservation evolves, is not deeply or extensively involved in his connections with reality. To make the transition from identity to conservation, there must be *quantitative* transformation. According to the rules of operation, identity (or compositions of qualities) can be established by simple perception without a deeper, more extensive involvement. The only kinds of quantitative relations that can be appreciated in this way are simple local evaluations like darker, bigger, wider, longer. These, Piaget stresses, "imply a partial one-way order, and not a complete seriation with ordered ranks and inclusions which can run in either direction". In a neurotic system, one-way order (identity) is the predominant form. The neurotic focuses on how he is or is not his Idealized Image without reference to the complexities of experience.

Conservation, as we see, implies quantity. Piaget says, "Quantity is necessarily based on a system of inclusions which takes into account the intervals, or the complementary classes." A child before the age of seven or eight may realize the principle of identity so that he perceives that a substance remains the same through several transformations. Then, at seven or eight, he comes to understand other principles of operation, for example, inversion, the capacity to change things around and change them back again. He learns about reciprocity and compensation, when one change is connected with other changes to produce a given result. At this point, then the notion of identity becomes operational: he sees that, in an event with change, nothing is necessarily added and nothing is necessarily taken away. He is appreciating the complexity of internal operations. This understanding is what Piaget calls the understanding of conservation.

The schizophrenic functions at the level of simple identity. Note, for example, a typical schizophrenic statement: the Virgin Mary was a virgin, I am a virgin, I am the Virgin Mary. As Arieti[5] has repeatedly emphasized, this is paleologic thought in which identity is made by an identity of predicates. But looking further, we may postulate that such a patient is immersed in what might be called mythical reality.[6] She is experiencing her unmarred, unconceptualized, direct feeling and is symbolizing this as the freshness associated with being a virgin. The "jump" to the class of "Virgin Mary" is her attempt to allay her aloneness in this process. She joins her predecessor, the Virgin Mary, in a class of people who are fresh and new. She is also exploring her relations to other virgins through feeling part of that class. As long as that class–identity with many virgins–is experienced, she can begin to see the differences and similarities of her special presence as a virginal state. However, she is unable to move any further in that, and, in a "failure of nerve", transforms her feeling into the simple perceptual set: she is *identical* with the Virgin Mary. Thus, she is not employing an operational notion of identity, but a one-to-one consolidation of the specialness she feels.

As we have tried to show, paranoid forms also focus to exclude the multiple aspects of ongoing experience. Paranoids tend to be reactive and deny the ambiguity of the multiple processes of experience. Theirs is an inability to engage in a real process of transformation. But through the continual immersion in uncertainty, some patients do begin to break out of the paranoid forms of identity-formation and gain a more ongoing ability to transform. The following is a lengthy statement made by one patient who was beginning to make this shift. I take the liberty of quoting this statement extensively because it makes clear the intimate problems involved in the movement from the paranoid forms to more engaged and forming strategies. In this statement, we can see that the main issue is one of how to contain the feelings of immersion-dispersal in order to make an organization out of them. This patient, a woman, reported:

Something quite surprising happened with me yesterday. I was talking to this guy in my office when suddenly I began to feel one of the anxiety attacks. This time it was different. Usually I feel that I am going crazy, that something outside is punishing me; I always felt it to be the result of the *action of some evil god, something from outside*, but this time I felt it something going on *inside me*. I related it to the experience of responding to food, to things happening to me. It was no longer something frightening, someone doing to me, I was trying; it left me shaking, trembling, but I never for a minute felt I was going crazy. I felt how different. It concerned me, it was unpleasant; I don't like it, it is disturbing but I never felt for a minute I was losing my mind, it felt very much physical; I did not feel someone hit me on the head with a club or in danger or threatened with being punished; it was physical. I had no understanding of it, but *it was my body reacting*. I always felt I was going crazy, someone had seized my brain, I was in terrible danger, had to flee before something terrible happened. I didn't like it. I was amazed at my own reaction, I felt if I could be alone for a few minutes, lie down and it would go away; it did not mean I was going crazy and had to be locked up; the feeling of fleeing, to run away is usually based on a feeling I cannot act, that I am a bad person or I am not going to let this evil force get me; now it was more like "I want to be alone" like an animal wanting to be off licking wounds, wanting to be by myself rather than run away from something strange. I felt a lot more confidence in myself, a lot less beating myself for doing something wrong, feeling whatever happening was inside me it was never a question of going crazy.

It was a feeling of having a *body*. I was there as a physical being, all self *contained*, I was surprised how I reacted no differently as if suddenly I got a cramp in a muscle. I was reacting to something, I was having a reaction, not something did something to me. I have a body and blood vessels, sweat glands, something happened, it all was a reacting. The way I used to feel was that something was saying no to me, some force saying get out of here, like a puppet jerked away by some punishing force. This time I felt something happened inside me, feeling it could just as well have been vitamin C I took in the morning as what this guy said. The kind of reaction I used to have was that sitting in a meeting some external law right or wrong had forbidden me to be there; I forgot I am not supposed to be involved in anything, I was reminded by the outside force. I was accepting the outside rule about what I can be interested in, punishment for overstepping boundary; I had none of that shift, I was *reacting*, whatever it was it was *inside me*, not in conflict with something else, part of me *I was* in control. It was a natural feeling, it was no more an external feeling of me; it was a natural thing, a different feeling in my brain from I am going crazy; it was distinctly different, it was locating in my body, not going crazy but *in body; when it is my brain it is as if somebody is manipulating my reactions*; it has rules: this can do and this can't. This time it was integrated in all of me, my emotions, my blood, my knees, me, it is a basic difference. It wasn't a thought or an idea, it was me feeling sick, not an idea, from my head to my toes all of me it was different too, in that before it was very frightening and I would feel this is terrible, "stop!" I will do whatever you say or what can I do to appease; there was not this thought of appeasement; it was scary, but I had no thought of what ritual I should do, go through to make it, whoever it is, stop; I realized I have a pain in my chest instead of saying it was an outside power; I said "I am hyperventilating and if I sit down and stop, it will"—And after, too, feeling how tired I was. I did not run from that, I realized, of course, I am tired, who wouldn't be?

Something else just came to my mind, something else that has been going on in me disturbs me because it is very different from the way I have experienced fantasies all my life. Whenever I would have had a fantasy I would be in a dream-like state; the fantasy seemed very real putting myself in a role and acting it out. Last night, and lately, very different almost like a fantasy, now it is my watching a picture in my head, visualizing it. Last night, Bob and I were moving some things from his old to his new apartment. Bob was looking for a parking place and was becoming increasingly angry. As he did, he was driving in ways I found somewhat dangerous, I was nervous. Instead of anxiety and oh my god I will be killed, I was sitting there feeling me and pictures going through my head almost as if a movie of a car being in an accident; no longer do I put myself out of the reality of the situation in a dream-like trance. I see pictures I am in a car visualizing what will happen rather than losing myself in a disturbed feeling. Almost feel crazy like in a movie flashback, I find my thoughts are taking a different kind of form. Instead of clutching seat of car crying "oh my god get killed" it is seeing a car hit a pole that's what could happen and I don't like that. It is like leafing through a book of pictures I guess the thing is so spooky but it is always me in reality there, I am not the mental image, I am here. Before, I would drift into the image and hardly tell difference between fantasy and reality. I have a strong feeling of myself existing and in control, thinking on the way here, you know that really it isn't bad, this feeling; it is much better to experience it that way. One thing I have been afraid of about travelling is, that I was afraid it would happen to me away from home; it comes, it passes, no longer an impediment to have that experience; I was afraid of it happening but it is not so bad I can have that, it doesn't really matter, it is mine, not something somebody else is doing to me.

As we can see, this woman is beginning to engage transitions in herself: being in situations which leave her on her own. These situations, characteristically, involve some confrontation with a man or with feeling that she is trapped and must engage the event unable to retreat to the safety of her home. This new step indicates a growing tolerance for experience; her previous intolerance for experience was often characterized by intense rage.

THE THERAPIST'S TASKS IN IMMERSION

The therapist of any patient becoming immersed in the continuum of experience has specific tasks. He must be alert to his patient's directions. He must be aware of the patient's developmental history. Each patient, of course, has particular closing patterns which he falls back into at moments of anxiety. I remember one patient, who each time she experienced some meaningful interest, would light a cigarette "to fill up the opening in her stomach". A patient may have a sexual fantasy, a desire to eat or masturbate, or a need to discuss compulsively how everything is "no good" in order to avoid engagement. The patient moves through immersion to these forms to a position of known consolidation and safety. At these moments, it is sometimes possible to help the patient feel the emptiness of his closure; that is, to experience his alienating. The patient's experience of the fact that he is in a state of alienation is, itself, an opening.

John Kafka[7] has pointed out that some patients experience too early in their childhood a demand for "task oriented behavior involving sensory compartmentalization at times when playful dream synesthetic experience was wished for and would have been appropriate". He speculates that the "difficulties" of these patients are "related to insufficient opportunity to cross and recross without challenge the 'transitional' area between synesthesia and sensory compartmentalization". Therapy, he emphasizes, "involved processes of reacceptance of, or perhaps acceptance of, or more specifically a learning to be less unfamiliar with, feeling of estrangement". Only out of such experience can the capacity develop for making distinctions and patterns in the immersion into ambiguity.[8]

CHAPTER 11

Focusing

THE MIRROR AS METAPHOR OF THE SELF IN IMMERSION

In immersion, the patient begins to make a transition from the kind of forming which takes social merging as its principal directive to forming which is indicative of an autonomous self. Of course, the autonomous self cannot simply emerge all at once out of nothingness; intimations of it must be felt first in a focusing by the patient to see where he really is. One of the symbols for this focusing process is the mirror. The mirror can convey just where the patient is with reference to himself as a self-focused organism. In literature and philosophy, the mirror has commonly been a metaphor for the self and self-reflection.

A person who develops his center in the outside world is continually in a position of looking for himself outside himself. He is, in effect, relating to the world as a mirror which tells him who he is and how he must be. If he looks at himself in a mirror and begins *to ask* questions about what he sees there, however, he is emerging as a person.

The particular meaning of the mirror will depend on the patient's current process. For example, it may confront him with his life in the old form: he may see in the mirror what he has been (so that, for instance, some patients see their gnarled or glum countenances); or it may confirm him in his actual aliveness and provide a feedback which further establishes the outlines of his separateness. But the mirror in its reflecting function acts with particular vividness at the time of self-creation. One woman wrote[1]:

> The most disturbing aspect of my environment was the quantity of mirrors. Having so recently been seen through the looking glass myself in psychic terms, I was nervous of mirror images and these were disconcerting—reflecting into one another and giving a series of similar pictures continuing unendingly in two directions. In one direction, the images were sharp and true, and the door at the end of the ward led through to the doctors' consulting rooms. This was the direction of sanity and quiet. In the other direction, the images were distorted, and at that end was the day room where a vivacious ex-variety artist lectured us on medicine; I remember especially her recommending pills containing white lead. That was the direction of nonsense and of noise.

Focusing on the mirror, this woman clarifies the differences between herself and others, establishing how she has used others to define herself. Through the mirror, she examines her previous relationship from a new perspective and in that act clarifies her new separateness.

In this regard, it is interesting to note the experiment by Gordon Gallup in which four jungle-born chimpanzees were observed first responding to their own mirror images as if it were another chimp. But by the third day of the experiment, Gallup[2] noticed that this "social response" had disappeared and the chimps had begun to use the reflection to inspect and manipulate those parts of their body they could not otherwise see: they used the mirror to pick food from between their teeth and to groom themselves. Apparently, self-recognition had emerged since they were now using the mirror largely for self-reference.

For the schizophrenic in the midst of immersion, there may be an experience of confusion about who is being seen in a mirror. When schizophrenics were experimentally confronted with distorting mirrors and asked to make the necessary adjustments (via electric motors) so as to provide an undistorted image of themselves, they were unable to do so. This would seem to suggest the magnitude and extent of the difficulty they are having in evolving a self-polarity out of their immersion. Their capacity to engage their personal complexity is minimal and they have difficult struggles in defining their separateness.

Laing[3] reports the manifest onset of one man's illness occurred when he saw someone else in a mirror, a "him" who was the paranoid persecutor attempting to kill him. This patient had doubtless come into experiencing himself as separate. He saw that there were multiple forming processes arising. His experience of this multiplicity led to anxiety about his separateness. He made a form: his-own-self-experiencing (reflection)–as-an-antagonistic-other-attacking-him reflects the anxiety of his experiencing his separateness. This sense of separateness is threatening his position in the alienated-social-other relationship on which he has depended as the man's feelings for his wife in the earlier chapter was poisoning his pride. Laing tells us he, as *he-in-action*, was determined to put a bullet through the reflection (his real experiencing self). The patient's direction was clearly not toward self-realization: he was in opposition to that more authentic organization. The anxiety over his own emergence led him to externalize and block his opening experience in the mirror while simultaneously clarifying the element of his conflict.

But more often, the mirror opens up the separateness. Hannah Green wrote[4] of her character, Deborah:

> After the session Dr. Fried went to her kitchen and began to brew some coffee. Mirrors and changes: Aren't all human eyes distorting mirrors: Here again as a hundred times before, she was standing between one person's truth and another's marveling at how different they were even when there was love and the shared experiences of many years.

Though feeling a real communion with her therapist, Deborah is able to see their differences. The analyst is, in effect, the mirror which allows her to see she is a forming process herself.

So mirrors reflect what one is, but also what one is not:

I think the mirror was for me a symbol or form of mental shorthand to express the awareness that we see ourselves as reflections in other people's eyes consciousness, and that our self may be distorted or damaged in the process.[5]

Elkish[6] has written extensively about the place of the mirror in psychotic process. She points out the psychotic fear of the loss of self in looking in the mirror. The separateness of the image challenges the alienated socially merged self. The psychotic also may, in trying to grasp himself in his reflection, see the possibility of drowning, like Narcissus, in that image.

(Note: As Horney[7] pointed out, the concept of narcissism as originated by Freud did not consider that there are differences in the *quality* of self-involvement. For Freud, narcissism was simply self-involvement, but Horney notes that egocentricity and self-aggrandizement are functions of fallen self-esteem. The grabbing at self in the mirror, the Narcissism, becomes, then, a necessity because the person does not really believe in himself.)

Frazer[8] has noted that in many primitive myths, there is the belief that the soul is or is not in the mirror image. He observes that mirrors are frequently covered at death because of a fear that the images in the mirror will be carried off by the soul of the corpse. The anxiety around separation seems to be reflected in this phenomenon where the person's being depended on the unity with the now dead other. According to Elkish, the mirror can also be used as a defense mechanism, the patient projecting onto the mirror image his confusion about sexual role. It can further be used to hold on to identity. In these various forms, participation in the mirror is the metaphor for personal sense of disorganization. But always central to the appearance of the mirror symbol is that it represents the new connection with self and is an articulation of the struggle of self-definition.

EXTENDING THE METAPHOR

When assets of self are poorly developed, there is the terror of self-reflection noticeable in some of the quotes above. On the other hand, as the patient reaches out to organize himself more coherently, he may use the mirror appearance as a focus to further contribute to his development; he may notice in the mirror parts of himself he has heretofore been unwilling to notice. (For example, one patient of mine carefully examined his anus and for the first time accepted the bodily reality he saw there.) Or we may see the mirror image alert the patient to a realization that he is there as fact, a *presence*, significant because it means there can now be a transposition from the patient's realization that he is presence to a sense of himself as an active event in which he is a constantly integrating-relating of his parts in connection with each other, the whole, and the universe. As one man put it, "I realized I could not know what other people were feeling about me as an object, but I could know how I was experiencing myself as an object." When he saw that he also realized himself as capable-of-feeling-that-he-was-such-an-object-among-other-objects. Paradoxically, he thereby *became more independent of his feeling of himself as an object*. He became someone who could have many different feelings: he had a position in space as an organizing process.

FOCUSING ON THE DIFFERENCE

As the mirror illustrates, immersion evolves through a focusing process. Focusing is actually defining the difference between the way the patient feels in the immersion (forming and opening) and the way he felt before (rigid, closed)—and clarifying what makes the two ways of being so different. The process of comparing old forms with new possibilities is often cast into the terms of a question about values. Frequently the patient at this stage voices an objection to all that is "materialistic" and "mechanical".

A neurotic pride system conceives the world under the construct of cause and effect, part to part—simplistically obscuring what is essential to organic life. There are, of course, too many relationships involved in human experience to be so easily encapsulated. In focusing, the patient becomes aware of the complexity that has been avoided by the mechanical, causal, and simplistic old structures. For instance, one patient wrote[9]:

> I'm going to be a lawyer and make lots of money and grow up to be as weak as my Father, as torn as my Mother, look ahead! Be a good little benjy franklin and don't despair, simply write down your virtues on one side of the page like this and then your vices on the other (that's a good boy) now add them up, divide by the fraction of normal life already lived (that's right, one-third) nice going, Benjy, you're doing fine, now multiply your abilities as scored by the IBM machine and factor by your various ambitions; what's the matter, Benjy, haven't got any?

One week after making this statement in his diary, this man was taken to the emergency room of a general hospital where he "presented a picture of intense fright, pressure of speech, ideas of influence and reference, and autistic thinking. Diagnosis based on clinical data and psychological tests was acute, undifferentiated schizophrenia." All week, as the entry from his diary attests, he had been involved in a process of focusing on the interfacial connection between his new form and the old forms of the family. In the quote, he raises, quite sardonically, the central issue of the difference between his new perceptions and the old form. He laughs painfully at the thought of being the acceptable lawyer, which is what his father is; and the father is seen as weak, even though he carries a designation society identifies as important: a lawyer. Another patient I worked with in the hospital looked at me one day and said, "The only reason I'm here in this hospital is that I murdered a few symbols." In his statement, the young man is also in the process of focusing on and destroying some of the symbols he has come to lean on. He had believed that in getting to be a lawyer he would find that strength he had symbolized in his father. But here he moves to reorganize his feeling by focusing and questioning his values, by making fun of false values which obscure what *he* feels. In the statement, he recognizes that he has no ambition in terms of these values, and in a deeper sense, no motivation to live. There is a poignant sadness behind this patient's sarcasm, but he is facing the issues. In the profoundest sense, he questions the worldly focus on finding out about people by making lists, using quantitative methods to evaluate the human soul. Though painfully, he laughs at the quantifying.

In a similar vein, Perceval writes[10].

I observed my family whenever they had a proposition against me which was not true in letter or in spirit, always introduced it with the words "of course". This style of speech I know to be proof of want of reflection. The attendance of Dr. Fox's servants was indispensable, but it was not *"of course"* indispensable that I should have their society all day, if I had been placed in proper circumstances: the servants were necessarily vulgar, but it was not *"of course"* that they should have been so low and vulgar as they were, even if no gentlemen could have been prevailed on to accept the situation.

The reality was that the servants were indispensable as long as Perceval was ill. It was not, however, the reality that he had to have them around every minute. His family had avoided the fact that the servants' presence for such extended periods was necessitated only by the inadequacy of the hospital conditions. They then mystified their avoidance of reality by affirming that *"of course"* it was necessary for the servants to watch him all day. Similarly, they avoided seeing the possibility of any variation in servants' abilities by affirming that no one of quality would take such a job. Thus the parents' *"of course"* signaled their inability to focus and make distinctions among different levels. They could not look beyond the surface of reality. Their *"of course"* froze reality at the level of their opinion and freed them from the anxiety of further exploration. Thus, Perceval's observation and focusing on his parents' behavior was an act of autonomous differentiation.

I remember an analogous kind of observation was made by a patient of mine who dreamed that he and I were sitting and talking with the light behind his head and that I was sitting in the "shadow of his head". At first he said he thought that I was sitting there to protect my eyes. Then I said I was doing this so I could examine and see the irises of his eyes. In discussing this dream, he noted that his first view was typical of his family where every event was considered "at the surface, in its most immediately obvious way". In his work with me, he was now considering the deeper, more focused, and directed meanings, one of which was that I was "examining" his eyes and not just protecting myself.

Bruner,[11] Piaget,[12] and others have called attention to the fact that a child begins to learn language after having come through a previous sensory-motor world characterized by the "action-linking process". This is the period which, as

I have stressed, is a beginning of forming. It is a time when the infant is processing reality directly, or pre-symbolically through his ongoing relationship with the mother.[13,14,15] The mother is transmitting the "feel of being" to him during this time. Bruner shows how, subsequently, the child starts to deal with the surface of things. He has most of his attention focused on the surface and generally cannot get into an appreciation of the deeper structures based on the invariant features of the environment.[16]

> In one experiment after another . . . we . . . see the younger child failing to solve problems by virtue of using surface cues while the older child succeeds by learning to respond to such "invisible" cues or "silent" features as relations, hierarchies.

To illustrate this concretely: I remember I once observed two children who were acting as captains of teams in a treasure hunt. There were six clues to where to find various objects. One child, a boy, immediately took his three colleagues and went looking for the objects themselves, reading one clue at a time; his anxiety and his need to win were overwhelming. The other child, a girl, gathered her teammates and read the clues, figuring out beforehand what each meant; she then assigned each member a place to go and retrieve the object. The little girl won easily, acquiring the six objects in the time the boy had only three. It was clear that the boy did not experience the situation as structurable. He lived it in its particularities and was an action-reaction model. The girl, in contrast, formed a plan and immediately, without knowing about cognitive principle, comprehended that this was the way to achieve the result most directly.

In the focusing that occurs in immersion, the patient begins to notice the difference between the surface and deeper invariant structures. Thus, we may see paradoxically an initial concern with the *skin*. But this is because the skin represents the first stage in delineating the patient as a subjective experiencing. There may be itching or increased sensitivity. As has been discussed, the patient has experienced himself previously only in terms of his outside, social objectness; that is, as an object that is not a subject in any way; the action of events has been outside him. Here, however, begins a differentiation which is subjectively experienced as a recognition of the body and its basic workings. "I-am-I" kinds of feelings appear with a sudden brilliance on a previously very drab scene.[17]

This subjective sense is part of the awareness of the actuality of what has always been. The patient may begin to speak of a hierarchical conception of life. There is often a quickening of intellectual process in which novelty is engaged and relationships immediately comprehended. The patient may inveigh against the absurd, meaningless conversations of people engaged in a pseudo-intimacy. He may notice that they have not really involved themselves in transforming their lives from feeling to meaning. What they claim they believe, he sees, is really someone else's opinion. Focusing with a new awareness of personal experiencing, the patient in immersion becomes acutely aware that other people do not live from their own authentic centers and he talks about how phony and unreal he finds them.

The person who is focusing also becomes aware of the falseness of his own pride system and sees the "synthetic" quality of the previous life; consequently, there may be growing appreciation of his own organicity, symbolized perhaps in a sudden preference for organic food, organic form in nature, etc. In the realm of human relationships, he sees he has been driven to placate people, to be one with everyone rather than separate; he finds he is tired of the compulsion to succeed and fit in. There is a quieter tone and a greater willingness to listen to others and himself.

Joan, one of my patients, came in one day talking about feeling "clouded". I asked her several questions about this: what was the feel of being clouded? and so on. As we talked, she said she began to feel "more and more cut off"; she said, "I feel quite conspicuous, as though I heard an echo to my voice; I feel stoned, light, as though I could fly away. When I was stoned last week, I felt more in touch with myself like the recurrent dream in which I feel either too small or too big. I feel as though I was losing my powers, as though I was asleep and could not wake up".

In the next session, Joan reported that she had felt sick after she left my office, and then during the week had begun to feel "more calm than ever in my life. I had many new ideas for painting and felt quiet. I could sit and read calmly." The rest of the session she spent discussing several new interests, including an interest in organic foods, and a growing relationship with her boy friend: "You know," she said, "next month we have been together a year; that has never happened to me."

With my focusing on the reality of the "cloudy", Joan became aware of being a separate entity. She felt stoned. I observed that, since she was feeling herself more now, she was also feeling how stoned she really was, and has always been. She confirmed this and increasingly became involved in the sense of being this separate entity, the stoned object. Interestingly, just prior to her expression of her sense of herself as an object, I had felt her to be very large in my perception whereas I was small. She was becoming more clarified in my consciousness as well.

As Joan fully experienced the focused articulation of her being, its outline could be more deeply known. What had then emerged was, to me, the essence of the mysterious process of transformation: her feeling for organic form. With the clarity about her separateness—her being-as-an-immediate-situation—Joan had developed, made the distinction between her shape and the world. She was feeling and being. This became expressed in her comments about the inauthenticity of the synthetic world around her and her feeling that she herself was more organic in the confronting of the world. Toward the end of the session, she began asking questions about me, about my personal history and interests. "I like this," she said. "After three years, this is the first conversation we have ever had."[18]

CHAPTER 12

Conflict: Defining "Reality"

Kuhn has pointed out that even with a serious crisis in the integrity of a scientific paradigm, the paradigm is never rejected unless a new one is available which will explain things more comprehensively; "the decision to accept one paradigm is always a decision to reject another, and the judgment leading to the decision involves the comparison of both paradigms with nature *and* with each other." As Kuhn makes clear, scientists will do anything rather than let go of an established paradigm: they will develop numerous modifications of theories to eliminate conflicts and will often resort to creating special cases, etc.

> A crisis develops when two world views are in essential conflict. Each paradigm is an entirely different way of organizing data and defining problems. The proponents of different views talk through each other using different definitions and even different words. They differ about *what* is worthwhile to know and *how* to know what is known.[1]

In the personality revolution, we have been examining compromise forms such as somatic organizations, hallucinations, and paranoid delusions which arise when the new structures are strong enough to create conflict with the old forms. Feedback information begins to be registered which indicates that the new structure, or paradigm, yields a more accurate picture of the personal reality than did the previous paradigm. For example, in analytic process, when the patient begins to see that acting in his own behalf rather than in a self-effacing form produces greater pleasure of longer duration, he feels conflict.

Conflict occurs at that stage (or at those stages) when the two opposing organizations are close to or equal in strength. "Strength" can be defined as the capacity of either organization to mobilize the capacities of the organism. When a person is moving from a center which has as a goal how *he* feels, as opposed to how others feel about him, each subsystem of his personality is influenced in that direction. Thus, he might want to improve his skills in a particular sport because he felt it to be self-centering, not because he felt he wanted to compete against or prove himself better than anyone else. (I am reminded of a patient of mine, a professional writer, who one day experienced an unusual sense of pride in something he had written. He told me he felt the work quite accurately captured what he had wanted to say, and that he noticed suddenly he was no longer afraid someone else would beat him to saying it. He had always been in a great hurry to write his message before it could be said by someone else. Now he found he could relax and be with himself and his feelings as he worked. The joy he felt in this was greater, he said, then the feeling of believing he was saying something special or different from what anyone else said.)

Conflict appears whenever old connections and old forms are still felt to be equal to the more self-directed integration. For example, a young man I had in treatment received a paper back from his professor with the statement, "You write with an enviable facility." Accompanying the paper were five articles written by the professor. The statement and the gift from the authority told my patient that he was a *capable person* who could write well. As he said, he suddenly saw that "there was nothing that stands between me and typewriter, but me." The patient became acutely anxious that this realization would unseat his feelings of being abused and impotent. I felt my task was to help him see the advantages of a new organization around his talents; I indicated that I knew he was anxious about the disruption of the patterns of self-obscuring which he had so recently been cherishing, but that this period of struggle was necessary and would be fruitful.

Another patient of mine experienced conflict over the question of whether or not to give her dog away. From years of much discussion on the subject of her relationship to her dog, we both knew her primary difficulty was that she could not control the dog. The dog ran her life, destroying her furniture and generally creating havoc in her home. She was unable to discipline him. In other areas of her life, we had observed a similar inability to make choices. She could not direct herself to any goal. She lived in the constant need to do as others required. The conflict over the dog mirrored and expressed her structure, but now in the direction of the new form, she had begun to feel a definite desire to discipline the dog, to choose when to leave it home, when to go out and walk it, and so on. This process meant confronting the dog, coming in direct opposition to an alive demand on her. Thus, she began immediately to think of getting rid of the dog, a solution under the old structure. Impulsively getting rid of him would have been a way out of the conflict of dealing with him in a direct, disciplinary manner which would involve using her capacities and working with the failures and success of discipline rather than avoiding the situation. I indicated that she should deal directly with the conflict.

TENSIONING AS CONFLICT

I use the word *tensioning* to describe the state of one system opposing and having some increment of power over another. The patient with the dog was in a state of tensioning toward maintaining her system of avoidance. The opposing system meant a centering-on-herself. She talked of the uncertainty the future held if one was active and independent. When tension rose, she would become ill and retreated.[2,3]

A tensioning was exhibited by a patient, Adam, who experienced his conflict in a physical realm. He was feeling considerable anxiety during the first years of his analysis when he tried to lie on the couch. Consequently, he had been sitting up for the past three years. Now, in his fourth year, he again was attempting to be on the couch. When he did, however, he still would become quite tense and often would doze off into a light sleep. I felt this sleeping was partly an anxiety process and a moving away, but also an important symbolizing experience because the sleep would frighten him and he would wake up with a start and feel, as many patients do, that he was "wasting time". I told him that I sensed from knowing his history that his problem of sleeping on the couch was connected with the fact that he could never be with his mother or father alone. They were both anxious and Adam felt frightened of what would happen with them if he let down his guard. Then, he began to let himself sleep; he was integrating his conflict at a level he, with his history, could tolerate. As he then moved into more experience of conflict, he began to experience an overall bodily tension. I encouraged him to confront these processes. I told him, "Only by letting yourself feel into this tension can you begin to be part of all that you are." He tried this a moment, then responded, "It is now crazy—the whole area above my eyebrows is hurting. I can't help but feel it there; it is an ache in that area—I feel I will walk out with that twitch." In the next session, he said, "Something very funny happened in the last session. It happened when you said that I should let myself feel the tension. I described it to you and I couldn't stop experiencing it all weekend. I saw how tense I have been all my life and I did not know it. I have been avoiding it." As the self-articulation phase continued, Adam observed more and more of his tension. He was aware of stomach pains and of his continual passing of gas. He particularly hated this habit, he said, because it reminded him of his father. Then, thinking of his father's uncontrollable habit of farting reminded him of his father's habit of uncontrollable rage and anger over the most trivial details. Clearly, Adam was afraid of his own uncontrollability, but he not only feared his own anger or rage, as he often admitted, but he also feared his needs. This became clear as we proceeded. Not long after his opening to an awareness of his tensions, Adam had dinner with his father. He told me later that he found they could talk now, and, although his father had not changed, he (Adam) had a *new perspective* and was not disturbed by his father's quirks of temper.

CONFLICT TOWARD SELF

With development, the self-centering process moves toward the new direction through tensioning and a glimpse of the possibility for self-affirmation can occur and can result in such dramatic statements as the following:

From ten thousand miles away I saw it as a blinding light: the important necessity of a Self: One's own single self. My original life—*what has happened to it*? Chaos was here—all around and in me that I understood in all my fragments. But was that all that one could ever know? What about the perfect planets, this earth people, objects: Didn't they exist and move? Couldn't they be known? Yes . . . but there has to be a knower, a *subject*, beginnings, direction, movement had to be from a single point; and ours is where we stand, alone, our being sui generis . . . Having discovered the necessity for it, I now began to see the significance of the self. Oh the million things you discover with the first touch of life! Almost before you've turned the key all the separate fragments of existence rush to fall into place. How can you see, think, speak, remember fast enough to keep pace? Is there nothing which doesn't fit here, even dying and terror and broken things? There is nothing of it unknown to you, and little that the average healthy man doesn't simply take for granted—but I had never before seen the sun rise. How could I have understood that the self is as significant as humanity. And this is not at all Freud's ego, but rather, as William James describes it, "what welcomes and rejects" (Freud's ego and superego, as I understand them are the neurosis).[4]*

I can compare this patient's new dedication to my own feeling when I am focused on a project. At those times, I experience a particular alertness to all features of my work. Everything I read or hear is related to the questions I am considering. I wonder constantly about what my next tack is. I am often irritated if I have to do something which diverts me from my central direction. I am always thinking and feeling in and out and around the issues, questioning myself about the validity of the point I am making; wondering if I am being over-inclusive in thinking something fits when it doesn't, and so on. Is it my momentary concern or is it something that is right? Certainly, it is exhilarating to be present in the open situation where it is possible to find answers or questions in a continual uncertainty that delights in itself rather than in turning away from the confrontation. But most thrilling is the grounding sense that I am engaging the uncertainty and within a certain area, I feel my own searching and my pending articulation.

---

*Her point about Freud's ego and superego is relevant. Freud's theoretical concepts postulate a kind of mind within a mind. They unfortunately do not appreciate that throughout nature, order is a function of organism as totalities. Freud's ego serves as an organizer of the rest of the system and is somehow conceived to be separate from the system. This patient is experiencing the ordering of her total being and is realizing that her distortion has been precisely such segmentation of her being; she sees that to have parts such as egos and superegos is an attribute of the previous disorder.

Part V

EXERCISE OF BEING: THE EMERGING PERSON

CHAPTER 13

Self-Articulation: Symbolizing

The conflicts between the opposing forms lead directly to the possibility of self-articulation. Webster's New Seventh Collegiate Dictionary defines articulation as: a) "The actions or manner of joining or interrelating," b) "The state of being jointed or interrelated." Since an extensive consideration of a definition of self would take us beyond the confines of our discussion, we will limit the use of the word "self" to that particular group of abilities, strategies, operations, or beliefs which have reached fruition in direct connection with the experience of the organism.

Self-articulation, then, is the pattern created by an organism which comes to see itself as being a whole; that is, which sees itself as acts and responses that follow a certain form. Self-articulation is the capacity to see the differences in one's way of being qua being.

SELF-ARTICULATION AS CONNECTION

What, I ask myself, is my unconscious? What, for that matter, is my consciousness? I am aware of a flow of thoughts, images, feelings, moods. I am aware of an atmosphere about myself which varies constantly. Images, thoughts, and feelings connect and emanate from that ineffable atmosphere. I feel all this is a resonating process, like the undulating rhythms of a wire under a constant tension. I relate to others, I am aware of now, and I am aware that this now is different in some ways from yesterday. The flow, I know, can evolve into a consideration of a wide range of events from my past. A burst of memory may come in the form of particular events, smells, or patterns. One form of being or thought may stimulate other forms, in a chain—but it all hangs together in the way I am being today, now. But how and why?

Suddenly I am aware of the image of a street; I know it from the village in which I spend my summers. It conveys a lonely isolation. I now am aware and feel a loneliness of which I was, until this image, only dimly aware. I know this image captures the passing time I feel as I struggle to put words to my ideas. Many other thoughts crowd into my being about what I do not understand about this moment—and what feels unclear seems suspended there in a state of expectant diffusion. I sense that I am a flow of patterns which the *I* that is sensing is part of and is aware of. The I that I am and that is aware is part of the system that is being and is registering in terms of those images and the feelings that are cast upon my consciousness. These images are forms of processing reality. I am aware of the patterns; the flow of thoughts are the present. Comprehending this, I feel that my confusion is a reaching out to the future in an effort to organize.

I know I am a continuity of being. I can write these words, using my muscles and the techniques of coordination in my hands and fingers. I have developed this skill through years of my interaction with the world outside my skin. The activity in which I engage the patterned movements coordinates the process I am as a being while my hands act as the effectors of expression. This is a structure: it has rules and forms which are more or less repetitive. I, as a structure, as an active process, use a language, itself a more or less fixed structure, with which I have learned to put together the uncertainties of the moment by moment being I am feeling. The permanent qualities of the language with their ongoing permanent and flexible meanings help me to bring into more articulate clarity the uncertainty of how my present feels. One more or less rigid form joins with the more indefinite forming processes we call experiencing.

The language structure is something we share. My personal experience we do not. The two together make a new shape, shape of meaning I share with you and, insofar as you understand it, it becomes a part of the larger form in which we, now, as a result of my act of writing and your act of reading, mutually participate. I can speak to you through the vagaries of these words and we can connect and become something bigger than I am alone; we can join the human race, history, culture, the eternal struggle.

I say we share these meanings–I sense it–but what is my sensing? I feel that we share my organization of what I am saying–I hope we do, anyway, because that further gives me a feeling of being whole, which is what I want. The image of the country village is my private form of connecting. I register a difference. The basic process which this image makes a bit clearer is still vague for me. I have experienced a private moment which I call loneliness after I shape it in the form of the image. I organize my loneliness in a form (the image) whose extensive connections only I may understand. I could perhaps share that hierarchy of connections with my most intimate friends, with my wife or with my brother; they would understand that place and that atmosphere, but as yet I do not wish to. The word lonely I could share with many others who would connect it with their own images and experiences.

My time is mine and I am there with my being. But what am I that I say time is mine. In saying I am a form–an *articulation*–of what I am: that is, I am alone and experiencing the private registration of my own sense of my time. What is the structure I call my being? My I? What is it that articulates a wanting to be alone? It is a process, registers as an experience which expresses an action of integrating the diversity. It becomes an I. What I am at this moment is organized and together with the universe–this shaping that I am is always part of my functioning in the universe–it is alone in that it registers how I am different now–is felt as being alone when I am into the kind of process that I am describing.

When another person comes into my purview, I recognize our structures as having commonalities of physical experience. As part of our shared humanity, I connect without question with another's being alone in a physiological form. I share similar experiences with my cats. But in areas of awareness and of perception, I do not have the commonality either with my cats or with other humans; these are areas of great uncertainty. I await my sense of experience when I am with another–a sense which I will know through our individual connections to each other, through individual connections to our individual past histories as they now are our connected lives, our relationship to our bodies, the cosmos, etc., at that moment. I do not assume I share any aspect of my separate existence except as we now evolve into that form through the event of our currently being together. Our unity awaits articulation from moment to moment. The flow of my thoughts, images, feelings reflects the ongoing tension of that being there with this other. As I am this, the other is also his thisness. In the intimate moment of his being himself and my being myself, the connecting makes for new structure and new process.

JOHN: HOMOSEXUALITY–THE SELF LIKE SELF

I am sitting with John who, as we have seen,* has been living out a form of homosexual relating. John has been telling me he wants to convince his new young lover to be faithful. For years, John has found his homosexuality unsavory and resisted acknowledging his interest in it. He speaks now of his objections to the young lover's activity and tells me that he has attempted to convert the younger man and make him realize the absurdity of his promiscuity. As he talks, John indicates his hopelessness about the lover since the latter has expressed the desire to have a baby and be a true woman to another man he has recently met. This upsets John because it conveys the severity of the young man's illness and, by implication, the severity of his own. As we talk, I hear in my consciousness the words of a song by Boo Dylan,[1] "When we meet again, introduced as friends . . ." What do these words mean in the context of my confusion? Gradually, I realize that I am connecting this song in feeling to another song by Dylan[2]–"She is just like a woman, she bakes just like a woman, she makes love just like a woman, but she breaks just like a little girl." And now, as I feel into this, I realize that the main thing John fears is breaking, losing control, being seen as awkward. For him, that is what a woman is. This prompts me to ask, "What is so terrible about wanting to be a woman?" John, shocked, stutters out that he is terrified of being feminine. It is so terrible to want to dress like a woman. In our work together over the previous five years, this theme has been slowly emerging. He has often dreamt of little girls. In his dreams, they are

*Chapter 4.

watching him shave or he is taking care of them. Often his feeling for them is quite tender. He has also in the past year spoken somewhat sardonically, of his desire to dress like a woman and today he has on what he calls his fancy dress shirt—it is adorned with a star on the left sleeve. I remember he had commented when he first wore it one year before that it was just like a woman for him to be decorating himself.

In this situation, I felt John's words were expressing his ongoing mode of processing reality. He was aided by the setting, the analytic situation, which had encouraged him toward the clear articulation of what he was. As a psychoanalyst, I am a process: part of the history of psychoanalysis, a disciplined worker, a training. I find I register pleasure when I understand how an order is present in nature, and particularly when it is being manifested in my patients. The structure of the participation in which I and my patients are acting reflects an ordering process. Our stance is one of awaiting what presents itself as the direction for our being together. This stance/attitude is a further reflection of the structure in which we are functioning and rules we are following which allow for the unfolding of the purpose of the structure: the patient's forming in the novelty of the present. My response in the analytic situation is a part of the connections the patient and I make together as we are open to the various aspects of the event of our togetherness, guided by and focused on the patient. We create a shape in our togetherness, moving toward seeing the revelation of the true form of the patient.

My experience with John helped him to order what was already an aspect of himself, but it also began the creating of a new order. In our work, he learned more about his old form in which he feared to experience the processes which he identified with woman. He came to feel both how he was afraid of what happened to him when he came near a woman and how much he wanted to be like a woman. He felt uncertainty and anxiety in any encounter with members of the opposite sex. We could say that his ordering process was an incomplete one, one of being open to considerable disorder because it was a system which was unable to handle one of the constancies in the universe, the presence of a different sex. John hated women because "they left their dirty hair on the bathroom sink and they were not compulsively clean in the kitchen" as he too was. His focus on excluding women emerged as a general avoidance of all phenomena which opened him to the complexities of his inner and outer existence. John's form of disconnection had emerged, for reasons both phylogenetic and ontogenetic, as a form we call homosexual. As he said one day, "Homosexuality is not having feelings." One of John's early memories was of being discovered playing with the genitals of his female cousin. As a kind of punishment, his mother told him of a man who had done this and then cut the body of the child into different parts and thrown them into the furnace. He commented often that this statement had frightened him to death.

In the period of self-articulation, whether it be on the global scale or on a more restricted one, many patients begin to speak about, or actually become involved in, homosexuality. As a fear, homosexuality can be extremely painful unless the positive features are appreciated by the therapist who can help him see that the feelings of homosexuality at this time are, in part, a thrust into the new reality. The form "homosexuality" is, then, a symbol which indicates that the new event is being experienced anxiously. The homosexual direction is, in essence, a move toward a "self like self". There are also aspects of desiring to fuse with another person. The first is a positive process, as with John whose one-night-stands were followed by his longer relationship and desire to help the sadistic, dark, young man. It is significant that after the affair with the dark young man, John became involved with a youth who looked like him, and that John was very tender to this alter self.

SYMBOLIZATION AND ANALYSIS

Winnicott[3] writes:

> In the healthy individual who has a compliant aspect of the self, but who exists and who is a creative and spontaneous being, there is at the same time a capacity for the use of symbols. In other words, health is here closely bound up with the capacity of the individual to live in an area that is intermediate between the dream and the reality, that which is called the cultural life. By contrast, where there is a high degree of split between the True Self and the False Self which hides the True Self, there is found a poor capacity for using symbols, and a poverty of cultural living. Instead of cultural pursuits, one observes in such persons extreme restlessness, an inability to concentrate and a need to collect impingements from external reality so that the living time of the individual can be filled by reactions to these impingements.

As Piaget[4] and others[5] have shown us, the child's first actions are a "looking at", followed by grasping, mouthing, holding, and the like. It has been established that the correlation of testing (exploration) behavior and feedback from the environment is the *modus operandi* by which a child gains his understanding of reality.

Vygotsky[6] pointed out the integrating process which language performs for the child. In his well-known sorting test, the subject has to arrange blocks in groups. The objects vary in width, height, color, shape (much as feeling and experience vary in quality in the immersion process). The very young child forms groups as "heaps", apparently unorganized pieces which he arrives at by picking up pieces at random—that is, a grouping by doing. Later, he forms on the concrete basis of "some other more complex relationship (produced) by the child's immediate *perception*". Then in the next phase, the child begins to group by what Vygotsky calls "thinking in complexes". A complex is a "family relationship". There may be a unity around one object with which the group shares a common attribute; or an integration around a theme. Finally, the older child begins to use logical categories of inclusion, exclusion, and overlap.

Essentially, the child first goes through the experience of participating with the different blocks and then he begins to *articulate* the relationships he discovers. In Bruner's terms,[7] the "experience must be prepared and organized better to fit the requirements of being handled by language."

Symbolizing is the process whereby the individual becomes an ordering of experience. Symbolizing involves analyzing and synthesizing the features of experience (the immersion) rather than merely registering the events as is characteristic of immediate perception in a child, and has been characteristic in the initial phases of the revolution. The capacity of symbolizing separates the immediacy of the event and localizes (focusing, conflict) the discrete features for actual clarification (articulation) which establishes a sense of presence in relation to the processes which are being registered.

Kelman[8] has called attention to the action of symbolization in therapeusis:

> Among the successes along the way are firsts. They become small milestones and points of reference to locate beginnings and endings of smaller and larger phases of the mutual therapeutic work. The success may be the first time a shy young girl accepts a date with a young man; the first time a man does not panic before a conference with the boss; the first time a woman has a fairly good night's sleep without pills; or the first time a male patient does not experience the analyst as a malignant authority. Guided by such objectives and ways of working together, the focus becomes less and less on working and suffering toward some ideal goal out there, and more and more toward realistic objectives in the here and now, in the realm of the probably and the possible.
>
> From time to time, patients will report firsts such as I mentioned above. The feeling that goes with such incidents is that of discovery and of a gift from emerging growing possibilities. These happenings can and do occur because both patient and therapist are no longer focused on proving and on improving. They are attending to the tasks at hand. Spontaneous emerging real selfness is the consequence.

These patients are involved in self-articulation. They are symbolizing and experiencing their articulation as a specific event in the evolution of their capacities (the "firsts"). As Kelman indicates, the analytic situation provides the structure through which the patient explores these symbolizing capacities. The following example may help clarify this process.

Joe is essentially in a form of compulsive heteronomy: he is always attempting to coordinate his situation so as to feel loved and accepted by others. He can only carry out plans if they are given him by an external authority figure. But when he feels himself governed by others, he rebels. During revolution, he relates a dream in which he is manhandled by sadistic, homosexual men in black, leather jackets. He rides in a boat in the dream with a black boy for whom he has some distant warm feelings. He says he feels at the whim of the men in the dream, feels dependent upon what they do to him. He does not consider that he can do anything for himself. At this point, he feels impotent and powerless to affect his future.

After another year of analysis and now into immersion, Joe has a dream of riding in a car with a friendly man whom he describes as "maybe homosexual, but very nice and interested in me". The car in which they ride "somehow" ends up in Harlem or Africa, surrounded by blacks.

The transformation from the sadistic treatment to the friendly homosexual treatment reflects Joe's growing appreciation and tolerance for the separateness and uncertainty which friendliness means. It also suggests a growth in his capacity to handle the closeness in the analytic situation itself, something about which he was initially quite afraid.

Meanwhile, the symbol black has become a minor but distinct articulation of what is coming. It is a part-process which points toward a gain in self-centering.

Joe is a wealthy Southerner raised in isolation from the surrounding black community: he has felt their joy and his dearth. Aware of this, one day I asked, "What comes to you about black?" His response was, "It is the nitty gritty people–sort of like you ain't got nothing, you ain't got nothing to lose. In a jungle tribe you don't know what's going to happen. It is a more alive situation. My own life where I know the rules as long as I play by the rules, nothing happens. With black, anything goes, watch out, have a good time, dance around with black women, attract nice women in a nitty gritty way. I am beginning to come to life, but when you do, you know you are alone, you are stuck where you are; it is being where you are. All my life I have been educated to be something other than what I am and in the process, held down."

Thus, with the symbol "black", Joe began the process of articulating his self. But this frightened him because it meant he would not be living just to please others. Shortly after the session, Joe performed exceptionally well in a task at the school he attended. The teacher and his colleagues went out of their way to tell him how well they thought he had performed. Although he was aware his activity had been initiated, in part, as an effort to please others, he also knew this time was deeply different because he had been spontaneous and open to the basic features of the work. He had found a degree of satisfaction for himself. This fact frightened him profoundly. He said, "I felt so alone standing there, having done this. I felt I did not know what to do with myself." There was a tensioning and the old system reasserted control: Joe promptly proceeded to get drunk so that he would "not have to remain alone."

In the session following this incident, he flashed the image, "a big pole sticking out of my chest, not a phallus, a bone-blood-vessel, alive, red, very strong, everything else built around that". This was another part-process symbol, like "black", which suggested a developing structure. It conveyed a thrust and an excitement. I asked him for more association to this symbol in an effort to encourage more self-articulation and the healing through the symbolizing process. But I did not get very far. That weekend, Joe was ill and had to miss the next session. There was malaise and fatigue, but no temperature. Diagnosis by a general practitioner was "virus". Evidently, the new process was creating a disruption of the old system.

The following week, Joe reported another dream:

It took place on one of the islands in Canada where we have a summer home. Our home is on the shores of Lake Yuion and there are islands two to three miles out. It is night. There is a black guy, an old guy and me. Three others and myself and two others. I thought they were trying to get back to the mainland; two rowboats were there and there was difficulty with them. The old man was a fisherman; he reminds me of you but it wasn't you. The black guy and myself were getting boats ready. There was an element of an enemy and we were watching out, not sure we could get back. We were set to go sneaking around in the dark getting boats ready. The fisherman was untangling his nets. We were just about to go and the sun came up. I was up on a rock looking down at two guys; the sun exposed what everyone was doing. It was very bright and it was difficult to see. It was palpable, filled the atmosphere. I had a large, sloppy hat with a brim shaded my eyes; I could see, others could not. I was pleased that I could see and that the others couldn't. Then the black guy said, "We don't have to look further for the enemy—there he is." Points the rifle at me. I look around behind me to see if someone is behind me, but see there isn't. It is clear they are pointing at me—two people pointing a rifle at me, but I was not understanding why.

Joe said this dream had to do with his feeling better than others. Then he added, "But I am tired of figuring all this out; ass kissing fucks me up. In an ass-kissing frame of reference, everything is the same, all feelings become neutralized. When I don't feel that way, those rare moments, some things are small, some are big. It is a much more eventful world. Right now, I feel a little sexually excited; it is another world, where everything is not flat and all the same."

The statement, employing perceptual symbols, conveyed Joe's experience of direct involvement. If it was to influence his total development, it would have to continue to be a principle of operation connected to all parts of personality. I asked him about the feeling of excitement again, hoping to stimulate the further self-articulation. He replied, "The sun was like a magnet, like the sun was a very bright kind of force that pulls me away, pulls me away from an interesting world in which I cannot stay very long, scary to think this is so strong; I feel disappointed that I am so attracted to it." The conflict again. The pull of self-effacing structure was there. On the one hand, in seeing and feeling into his new form, Joe found it exciting and appreciated the novelty of this new world where everything was not leveled as it was in the old; but, on the other hand, getting to the mainland, into that actual world, having to confront the brightness of life was too much for him. In the dream, he shifts back to the old form of being heteronomously absorbed by outside centers, symbolized by the sun. Joe's disappointment in being "attracted to it" was an evidence of the evolution of his new structure. It indicated that enough of it was there for him to begin to pull against it.

Kelman[9] asserts that the basic level of all symbols is pure fact experience. This is a presymbolic level which is the pure silence of being in a moment of involved uncertainty and process. From that still point, we may initiate the action: that is, we realize ourselves and derive pleasure through our integrating process: non-verbal, verbal, conceptual, nonconceptual, images, or dreams.

SYMBOLIZING BLOCKS: EXPERIMENTAL DATA

Dyrud and Donnelly[10] have performed an interesting experiment which demonstrates that the process of symbolic self-articulation can be stimulated even in acute schizophrenia. They reported they had found a patient on their ward who spent most of her time watching television. To help her develop some initiative, they required her to adjust her own television, select programs, focus and adjust the set. They wrote, "The mobility initially required only to watch TV, became an independent self-initiated source of gratification." The patient, as a result of this symbolizing activity, began to explore the entire hospital. She came to experience her own movements, wishes, and feelings. The exercise of her symbolizing processes had helped her to realize that she could perform. This was an event which established her as a process and as a new possibility for the direction of her life.

Perhaps even more dramatic is an example which appears in Sara Sheiner's paper,[11,12] "An Investigation of a Learning Block in Schizophrenia." Dr. Sheiner points out that schizophrenic individuals often involve themselves in pretense to avoid the deep feeling of inadequacy we have discussed. They sometimes behave arrogantly and alienatedly, are detached and superior to all the events around them in order to cover over a deep pain and anxiety about some feeling of internal deficit. Dr. Sheiner reports that as the need for pretense with one patient in long-term psychoanalysis lessened, and trust grew, the deficit made its appearance: the patient could not conceptualize space. She could not make a map of how to get to the office, could not make an ordinal sequence, count change, or categorize—all symbolizing activities. The deepest feeling the patient expressed in her behavior was that she believed she was unable to learn and so had to conceal her inadequacies in the pretense; she was humiliated by her inadequacy and humiliated by all that her inadequacy "made her do". Detailed and painstaking work by Dr. Sheiner was necessary to help the patient first realize and then accept, the deficits. As she accepted them, she could be helped to learn that she could learn. This resulted in a new sense of her real capacity to symbolize.

Eleanor Galenson's[13] description of children's play provides some further analogies to symbolization and self-articulation as it occurs in the analytic process. Dr. Galenson emphasizes the self-creation value asserted in the child's continual exploratory articulation of shapes in his play. These are prelogical processes brought into a presentational symbolism. She notices that the symbolic play of disturbed children tends to be "narrower in variety, richness, and originality. There is also a greater proportion of direct expression of impulse via bodily movement." This fits with the observations of Kagan[14] who has observed that hypermotoricity interferes with "reflectiveness" in young children and apparently contributes to the delay in language development and linguistic ability. The rigid forms of such children is the motor reaction which blocks an openness to coordinating experience into symbolic forms.

In the analytic process, the patient is helped to be open to what he feels rather than oriented to keeping his feelings to himself. In his immersion in feeling, the patient begins to transform events into symbols and concepts which unite him with the analyst and the world. He relates present events to the past, to memories which are similar and different. He talks of books he has read, plays he has seen, people he has met. These symbols allow him to become an active form of actually relating, forming himself.

ARTHUR: SYMBOLIZING INTO SELF

Arthur, a thirty-five-year-old patient, has been talking about the fact that the weekend before, while working as a volunteer in a city hospital, he noticed that the doctors in the hospital were quite self-inflated. The nurses, he said, knew what to do with a very sick patient: they took him directly to the intensive care unit. The doctors, on the other hand, stood on "ceremony", followed the rules and took the patient first to the admitting area. Arthur is caustic in remarking that the doctors with their big words were involved in their petty egocentricity and were missing the fact that the patient was dying. I am aware as Arthur talks that some of this venom is directed at me, that he is saying that while *he* is dying I am not doing enough for him. I am not taking care of him. It is an old plea. I am not supporting his dependency needs to avoid being on his own. But I sensed a very strong thrust in his seeing how he is involved in a system of values which prevent him from concerning himself with himself. For most of his life, Arthur has focused on the way he stood with others and he has always needed some woman to take care of him. He has a life-long fear of being alone. The next session, he comes with the following dream:

It was a dream within a dream. I was relating the dream to the analyst in the dream. I was walking down the street and saw a street fight. In the street fight, I see a couple of people not so much beating the guy up—I don't know if you have seen street fights; one way to fight is to pull the jacket down and then the person is effectively in a strait jacket. That is what was happening here. An unidentified person goes to help. He motions to me; I don't understand. I keep walking. Then the realization comes to me that the person was signalling me for help. I didn't understand the signal. Then the dream moves to my talking to the analyst. We were sitting on a couch similar to the one in your waiting room. I don't want to say you; he was wearing a suit, sitting straight, not rigid. I was feeling very comfortable. He was right next to me. I could see him and talk to him. He seemed to shift places. He was no longer there. He said something. I said, I'm sorry, I didn't hear you; again it happened, and a third time, he gave no answer. I began to worry. Am I losing my hearing? I was not receiving the hand signal either and I felt distressed. In the third part of the dream, in this room of the analyst, there were his two children. The analyst was making a point of awareness using as an example his daughter; she was ill and they had trouble waking her up. They would take a puppy, hold it close to the girl and the squirming puppy's tickling the kid's chest was the way they aroused her.

In his discussion, Arthur emphasizes the "not-hearing" aspect of the dream. This was clear to both of us. It is also clear to both of us that Arthur is avoiding doing anything for himself in this dream. He noted that there is a moment in the dream in which a figure comes between him and the analyst, clear evidence of these avoidances. As we worked through the dream, we emphasized the negative, or what would be called resistance, aspects of Arthur's structure; I begin to get a feeling that there is more here than we are catching. I find myself thinking about our last session and Arthur's strong emphasis on trying to get closer to reality. I feel the not-hearing as part of a larger, more inclusive form, which includes a new process. I say suddenly, "All this we say about the blocking out and not hearing in the dream is there, but let's look at it a different way. This is the first dream you have reported in the two months since the summer vacation. This report is part of a new connection with yourself. There is an awareness of the call for help in several instances and that is new for you. There is also a progression in the dream to more and more intimacy. The cry for help moves to the directness of the couch scene with the analyst and then the close connection between the dog and the little girl."

With this statement, I feel I am outlining the form of Arthur, a form which includes his *presenting* the not-hearing. I stressed the novelty of the appearance of this form which can "see" not-hearing. I defined the elements of the dream and the experiencing process, but in a way which brings out their unity of operation. This has to do, in fact, with *hearing* the importance of helping, caring, and listening. Arthur began immediately to explore how he felt bound by terrible fears of hearing what is bothering him. He said he is desperately afraid that if he does hear, he will go "insane". He connected to the fact that his procrastination in dealing with himself was very much like that of the doctors in the emergency room. While someone is dying, they are involved in their neat, precise, trimmed words and do not see the problem. He is no different; he does not hear himself. But I stressed that the dream with all of its not-hearing is, at the same time, a feeling into *what* he is not hearing, namely, his growing intimacy with himself. It is symbolization and articulation of his forming into a hearing entity.

Arthur goes on to describe how he feels about not hearing the call for help in the dream. He is aware, he says, that he is tied to a mode of being which takes him away from his own experience. He has the recurrent memory that in the hospital that Saturday night two weeks before, he had had to cut the clothes off a man because that was the only way to examine the man's broken leg. He comments that he could have done this only by releasing himself from the false values about the monetary worth of the clothes. He had to keep the importance of real values, the value of the man's life, in the center of his attention. He sees that he must begin to deal with himself by letting go of the false values he had held to be so important because of the safety and refuge he thought they offered him. The volume of his voice and the speed of the flow of his speech triples as he talks about how he feels bound up in his old values.

For Arthur, the weeks following this dream are filled with thoughts of being able to work on a play he has been procrastinating over for a decade. The subject of the play is procrastination. But Arthur is still afraid of being in the room alone confronting his anxiety and terror on a blank sheet of paper. We talk about this and he has the following dream:

I was riding on my motorcycle and it stopped. I looked in the gas tank, an illogical place to look since with the bike, there is always a reserve gas supply and one only has to flip the lever to let the gas in. In the tank I saw dried out gas which was crystallized.

The crystallized gas, I suggest to him, symbolizes his new thoughts of himself as a person of value. They are making it increasingly impossible for him to run away (on his motorcycle) from his life. In the dream, Arthur feels the process of the new taking over and the old collapsing. Later, he comes upon a consequence which is less palatable; he begins to have the recurrent fantasy that he is grabbing someone by the neck, shaking him viciously and violently, and screaming, "Can't you hear what I want?" As we talk about the feeling that goes with this fantasy, a very complicated situation emerges. I suggest that he is afraid that his screaming "I want" will become his state of being. He acknowledges that if this happens, he fears he will have too deep a sense of being involved with himself. If he feels that deep an involvement in his own wanting, he fears he will have to confront the actual conflicts of his life: his guilt for abandoning his wife and son and the pain of seeing the unhappiness of his child, a pain he finds virtually unbearable. He sees he will have to feel his actual unhappiness.

There is no way around these consequences, however. Our human help stands there with our patients at these moments. We too have known such problems and can only help our patients realize that life is what it is, neither beautiful nor ugly. These are the moments we come together beyond our masks and share the fact that this other, whom we have defined as patient, is indeed a fellow traveler on a journey which began in nothingness and will end for both of us in a similar way in a not too distant future.

As Arthur developed a self which he could appreciate was an operative entity, he started to gain a certain clarity about how he had functioned in the old form. He connected one day:

When knowledge of compulsion becomes awareness, you can sit back and watch yourself in actions. Witness your own compulsiveness—to dive into a thing in which I didn't want to get involved. Like that girl I picked up at the bar two or three months ago. I acted out the whole role. What the fuck was I doing there? I certainly did not need the sexual thing. Joan was waiting at home. It was not an ego thing because, to use a cliche, she was a pushover. I was acting out the whole compulsive thing, the drive to that, whatever that may be; you could say I did not yield to it last night when I almost went compulsively into that partnership with Jane. I saw myself saying I should, why not? At the hospital when that nurse hurt me by saying I should not be in there with the patient, I was hurt and had the compulsion to hide, to run away into the corner. It hurt bad, it was a real down trip I had to fight it and say, "Who was the doctor who said that?" I did not want to pursue the issue and deal with the situation; I wanted to run away compulsively as I do when I am hurt.

It is like when Timmy [his five year old] or the other kids have to go to the bathroom. They do a traditional war dance; they will do anything rather than go to the bathroom; they are torn between going to the bathroom and urinating and compulsively continuing what they want to do. I had the compulsion to run and hide, but a little voice inside was saying bullshit.

Arthur had evolved what some would call an "observing ego". In the process of his own forming and symbolizing, he has come to feel into the comprehension of a whole. He knew himself as an action-process and felt his own emergence as a constant connecting process.

THE ANALYST AND SELF-ARTICULATION

The moment of a patient's transformation into an emerging self is perhaps the most dramatic in psychoanalysis. Many analysts are jarred deeply by the experience and feel a new hope in the therapeutic process as well as in their own capacity to learn. Of course some therapists have been known to become jealous, seeing their patients becoming so self-affirming, since it poses a contrast to their own cynical intellectualizing; they panic and terminate the patient's therapy, unconsciously feeling that a patient who turns toward life will also turn toward them and be open to the relating experience of analysis. Such analysts may sense this to be the beginning of some new and uncertain (and consequently frightening) process, a process which has never been described to them in the literature because it is indescribable; because it is nothing less than the process of two open human beings spontaneously responding to each other's novelties and willing to share in the creative activity of making meaning together in the flow of the moment.

At such poignant moments, the analyst may hear his patient say, as Arthur did, "It hurts to see this," or "I feel lonely," or even "I don't feel like talking today," and he must resist the therapist's impulse to avoid his own uncertainty by analyzing or clicking off the diagnosis, "The patient is blocking." When silence is a form of resistance and blocking, patients, more often than not, don't say they don't feel like talking, they simply do not talk. So in many cases, it is better for the analyst to remain silent, because the patient—who has just spoken from his self—can hear in that accepting silence what he has articulated.

CHAPTER 14

The Structure of the Self-Articulating Symbol

The nature of the self-articulating symbol can be said to reflect the level of the individual's development at the time the symbol appears. This is because each individual symbol functions as a kind of game with special rules played in a closed area which is the capacity of the self.

The holistic, self-clarifying, and self-establishing character of symbolizing itself has been evident in the substance and direction of the process we have been discussing. We have, for example, seen how the mirror as a symbol can become a statement of the way the alienated person first finds self in the world. The Dyrud-Donnelly experiment with the schizophrenic girl and the TV set has shown us the symbolizing process of a severely disturbed patient through a manual task: as we observed, this symbol exercised the patient's capacities at a level appropriate to her capacities and, thereby, opened up her particular existence to other connections. We have also seen that with the patient, John, who began his self-articulation by first caring for plants, then for a dog, before he became involved with the dark, young male lover. In terms of human relating, the relation with the last was meager at best and we note that John's attempts to "improve" and "help" his young lover were symbolic of his dominating, mechanistic need for control, but they were also representative of a move to help himself. And later, as we observed, John found a young man whom he felt he could trust, one who "looked like him", thus, a relationship that accurately symbolized the true development of this self.

Similarly, for Arthur, "not hearing", and for Joe, "black", were symbols which indicated the extent to which they had come in their self-emergence—but also implied the limits of that emergence. Indeed, the subtle interplay between the extents and limits of the symbols in self-articulation is central to the process, as can perhaps be illustrated by the following detailed example.

THE PRISONERS

In studying[1] a group of adolescents who were incarcerated in a naval prison, I observed that they had a particular fascination with fitting together and repairing cars. I noted that functioning with their hands, putting the machines in working order and "seeing the whole thing work" gave these young men an evident satisfaction. They would tell me, "It makes me feel good inside to know

I can fix it to run right." I subsequently learned that for many of them, this experience in auto mechanics was the first time they had ever had any feeling of being interested in anything—and the first time they had ever been able to feel satisfied with themselves in the performance of a task. Their descriptions of their work conveyed an accommodation to their own enjoyment potentials, a relaxation of tension, and a feeling of self-sufficiency. They had obviously moved into an area where they felt they could locate themselves, articulate themselves, and enjoy the presences they created of themselves as a result of their activity.

On closer examination, it was apparent that these adolescents felt like they were running the show when they fixed cars: they did not feel pushed, forced, or told to do what they did not want to do. They emphasized again and again that they were "doing it themselves" and obviously felt particularly capable at this level. This level represented a point at which they could articulate their diverse and disorganized feelings, a nodal point for the integration of their personalities.

Kelman[2] states, "The symbolizing process is an aspect of integrating." He emphasizes that integrating is the *goal* of symbolizing. Symbols are chosen which will adequately convey the essential fact of *what* is being integrated as well as the nature of the integration. Webster's New Collegiate Dictionary defines "integrate" as "To form a complete or perfect whole; unify; as, to integrate the plots of a play." Or as one of the prisoners put it, "I like to get it running, have the satisfaction of seeing it run smoothly, effectively, and fast." Since these young men had felt trapped, subjected to the whims of outer powers and their own uncontrollable states, feeling powerless and confused in their world, through the symbol of the car they were integrating and attempting to form what were for them meaningful wholes. By fixing the cars they were fixing themselves at the same time. "I feel that I don't run myself; I feel that I'm run by something and you're no good to nothing unless you're in an operating condition."

We note that the process these adolescents were involved in was a different one from that observed by Wallingá,[3] who discusses cars as offering "some gratification and a seeming opportunity to prove oneself to the peer group". Wallingá stresses the masculine symbolic value of the car and one particular aspect, power. What we are emphasizing here also differs from what Bond[4] speaks of about flying, when he says:

> The bodily significance of the aircraft leads one to the conclusion that this display of "High Spirit" is an unbridled exhibitionism, a flaunting of phallic power . . . The symbolism of flight as intercourse makes clear the incestuous gratification appropriate to the unconscious thinking of this period. The closeness of death is the part of the game that makes it worthwhile and one is struck with the defiant quality lying just beneath the surface.

The prisoners in my study did become involved in this sort of feeling when they raced their cars, but blanket interpretations like those of Wallingá and Bond tend to be overly concrete: they overlook the positive dynamics of such behavior. The process exhibited here was more holistic. The focus of these men was, first, to get the cars fixed and working as well as possible. "If something is broken, I can fix it" or "I know every part and can take it apart and fix it myself." Erikson[5] has commented that American youth operates generally under the ideal "functioning without friction":

> As an adolescent and man, however, he finds himself confronted with superior machines, complicated, incomprehensible, and impersonal: dictatorial in their power to standardize his pursuits and his taste. These machines do their powerful best to convert him into a consumer idiot, a fun egotist, and an efficiency slave and this by offering him what he seems to demand.

The prisoners' fascination with power through smooth functioning was this but also a system-integrating principle, though it clearly constituted the guiding aspect of their pride systems as well. When the ideal of smooth functioning was achieved, they found meaning and felt the completion of their idealized images.

Thus, it would appear that these young men were caught in two ways. The natural aspect of developing into an adult presented puzzles they felt were beyond their abilities. Their backgrounds were inadequate to provide them with the proper resources for openness and, as a result, new situations created considerable anxiety. Their pride in "smoothness without friction" and "playing it cool" led them to restricted personalities; and this pride determined that their experience of even the minutest differences in life was threatening. They were constantly afraid and on guard, and this caused them to restrict their life experiences to those which fit the pride image.

It is not to be construed that these men were frozen at any particular cognitive level, but that, dynamically, they had become involved in a symbolic cognitive process which seemed to be related to the central principle of their personality functioning. The process of fixing an automobile is, at its basic level, an organizing of parts into a working whole. Observed simplistically, this is a concrete process and involved arranging and coordinating the specific actions of specific parts joined in specific ways. Cognitive models are numerous, but the one that seems most appropriate is that presented by Piaget.[6] The type of thinking exhibited by the men is similar to the kind of thinking Piaget calls[7] "infralogical grouping", which "can be conceived as structural homologues of the logical groupings; they characterize the cognitive structure of the middle-years-child when his operations apply to the physical world of spatiotemporal wholes and parts, spatiotemporal positions, and displacement of positions and the like." Piaget's infralogical operation involves "analyzing and resynthesizing . . . the object" and "joining together . . . parts into progressively more inclusive wholes". There is an important additional capacity normally developed in the mature logical thinking of later adolescents. "The assignment to a class [becomes] completely *independent* of the location of these objects in space and time" (italics mine). The satisfaction the adolescents at the prison felt in fixing automobiles apparently resulted from the aesthetic completion of a model they had in mind. This model fulfilled many of the characteristics noted by Piaget for his infralogical type of thinking. But it did *not* involve aspects of the more mature thinking. The parts were organized into wholes which were totally *dependent* on the presence in the time and space of the object in front of the operator. I observed that these young men, in fact, rarely became interested in concepts of automotive engineering or in the dynamics of motor functioning, concepts which would have required them to be able to abstract. Their overall system-principle of smoothness apparently had resulted in a restriction of their normal exploratory capabilities as growing adolescents, as well as a restriction in their abstractive processes and their capacity to extend their self-articulation beyond the limits of the machine image.

Nash[8] states, in a recent paper, "The machine has been a compelling image" in the history of science; he goes on to note:

> . . . with the seventeenth century advances in the science of mechanics the universe itself came to be regarded as a machine and men as *l'homme* machine. Descartes' psychology, based on the idea that man is part machine, was succeeded by the more thorough-goingly mechanical psychologies of Hobbes and Hartley, psychologies fashioned under the influence of Galilean and Newtonian dynamics respectively. The mechanistic approach to problems of psychology persisted vigorously though mechanics ceased to occupy a pre-eminent position in science.

And Nash further states:

> Challenged by new and puzzling observations, the student of nature gropes about for ways of restoring order to his world. He may seize a familiar experience seemingly alien to the problem at hand and represent the problem in terms of the more fully understood solution.

CONCLUSION

The car, for the young prisoners, represented an opportunity for self-articulation as well as a limit to it. It exercised their capacities: it organized their sense of disruption, and it concretized and restricted the entire process. Having clarified and focused their integration at this point, there was, of course, always the possibility that any one of them could become aware of the connections of his car to the world of engineering and design in the larger world, and thus extend himself beyond the immediate image. However, for the moment, in the structure of the symbol lay the structure of their current integration.

CHAPTER 15

Conclusion: The Evolution of Complexity - Toward Autonomy

Each time someone experiences himself as a relating process, he establishes himself as a complex fact. His alive connectedness serves as a feedback to the totality of himself and the connectedness makes him more alive. This circle creates his presence.

The self-articulation process itself provides the principle of this connectedness and the inherent sense of self on which we build our awareness and openness to the world. With the evolution of complexity, through self-articulation, an increasing number of connections are made among aspects of the self. These connections build the very subsystems which they express, thus creating a "sense of self" which becomes, in turn, an experience of autonomy.

Ellen reported to me one session that she was taking particular delight in a magazine article she had authored. She had presented the elements of an event in a different order from the one in which they had occurred. She had written about parts of the action after describing the conclusion of the event. The particular pleasure was that she had asserted her position, had created a form herself instead of merely being governed by the outside action. Ellen's pleasure derived from having expressed the unique relationship she had with the data. This was an exercise of her symbolizing capacities, but it was also an exercise of her autonomy. She made symbols through her new structuring of the event and was not simply being the reactor copying an external form. In the simple act of reacting, she would have exercised her writing subsystem but in the active form she exercised not only that capacity but also her capacity for relationship to her other internal modalities, that is, feeling something about the particular event and its meaning to her, her past, her friends, etc. She engaged herself to create a new holistic form. In writing in the non-sequential way, she was connecting the facts of the time sequence with other forms of organization that she felt were being realized. She was making meaning with words which reified the connections. The connection process and the connections themselves were an evolution in her complexity.

The differences between levels of complexity are the differences in the degree to which a person is open to experiencing the world as it is. A striking example of the hierarchical unfolding of these levels appears in the statement of a patient who had undergone five psychotic episodes. She related her experience in terms of a recurrent dream[1]:

I have climbed up and reached a point where the stairs are missing and there is a gap to be jumped, and it is impossible to get across. In the old days, this was an acute nightmare, and I was on the verge of falling when I woke up. From the tremendous emotional fear that it can produce, I assume that this dream has an infantile origin. Perhaps it related to this fear of falling or being dropped that is experienced for the first time immediately after birth. After I had recovered from my first mental illness, the dream changed. There was still a moment of fear when I reached the danger point but terror was gone and I never reached the point of falling. I was no longer alone and helpless, there was always someone at hand to help. The dream comes back from time to time, but by now I do not usually need help. Sometimes I decide it is not essential to go on, I can return the way I came or find some other way down. Sometimes I can get across the difficult spot unaided and occasionally I have even helped someone else across. I do not get real nightmares any more.

This is concrete evolution. Initially the dream was a nightmare: the patient was unable to deal with uncertainty. After the revolution of her first illness, she emerged from her terror to a state in which she is able to tolerate fear. She does *not* fall. This is a definite shift: she can sustain herself in the face of the immersion without falling into disorganization. There is someone there to help her and she has focused enough to support herself and aid in her own understanding of the problem. This meant a tensioning in the system favoring her own development: she had shifted her side in the battle; she had joined elements through self-articulation, and was definitely stronger after the first psychotic episode. She faced conflict alone. In the last part of her statement, she indicates she has not needed help in the dream. She is more fully with herself, more autonomous. She is the originator of a strength which, in the language of the dream, is symbolized by her helping herself. In the final lines, she shows her differentiation has proceeded to a more complex form of organization: she has flexibility and *can even help someone else.* In sequence, this last move represents a growing strength that has accrued to her through her willingness to explore, to be open. She is still dealing with old issues, but is no longer having the sense of inadequacy in facing the uncertainties of which the nightmares had symbolized she was in terror.

The building of the self is a development of a more complex organization of strength in which different functions begin to unite around a higher order of preferred configuration.[2] This occurs because, through the development of connecting processes, it becomes possible to engage wider areas of reality. As the wider areas of reality open up, change-processes develop a momentum of their own.

Susanne Langer has illuminated this momentum in an interesting statement about the evolution of the mind[3]:

To trace the development of mind from the earliest forms of life we can determine, through primitive acts which may have vague psychical moments, to more certain mental acts and finally the human level of "mind", requires a more fertile concept than "individual", "self", or even "organism"; not a categorical concept, but a functional one, whereby entities of various categories may be defined and related. The most promising operational principle for this purpose is the principle of individuation. It is exemplified everywhere in animate nature, in processes that eventuate in the existence of self-identical organisms; it may work in different directions, and to different degrees; that is, an organism, proto-organism, or pseudo-organism may be individuated to a high or low degree, in some respects but not in others, and anomalies of individuality–double-headed monsters, parabiotic twins, as well as properly semi-individual plants and animals–may arise by imperfect or by normally only partial individuation. Under widely various conditions this ubiquitous process may give rise to equally various kinds of individuality, from the physical self-identity of a metabolizing cell to the intangible but impressive individuality of an exceptional human being, a Beethoven or a Churchill, who consequently seems "more of an individual" than the common run of mankind.

Every move from one level to a next is a hierarchical unfolding.[4,5] A new level of complexity does not emerge from nothing. We do not become Buddhas overnight, nor do we solve our problems all at once. The change in the capacity to engage possibility must be based on the willingness to endure anxiety. Gradually one grows toughened to uncertainty and each new level emerges out of the incapacities of the previous level.

Any given level of complexity includes the way a person experiences his ability. It includes the way he relates to other people, the way he uses objects, how he feels about time and his personal space. The developed capacity for engaging is a reflection of the level of integration of subject and object. The object is then the subject in that the two cannot be separated. Organizing is the unified subject-object ordering process as it takes place through self-articulation (symbolizing). The level of complexity of self-articulation equals the degree of autonomy. Thus we can view autonomy as a certain overall capacity or mode of functioning in uncertainty: it is the level of overall capacity to remain open, to engage anxiety, and to make new forms.[6]

The ultimate autonomy (or freedom) is discussed in eastern religions where there is the concept of no individual self, but human beings as aspects of the Self, the one in All. Perhaps that is a good description of what occurs when the experience of the human organism is one of openness. The ultimate possibility of this may be represented by the sage, who makes a total commitment to openness and the continual experimentation with forming, that is, playing with forms. Flowing with the presence that is change and process, which is to be what *is* in the universe, to be and to be open when we are not clinging to our notions of individuality but realizing that what we call change is the functioning registration of difference, which is the flow or relating process and a participation in the world, when, that is, we are not infatuated with the "I" experience of our separate existences, and are a pattern of the *flow* of all of reality: seeing what we are is an aspect of the All.

* * *

In biology, two special factors[7] have been important in the general evolution from simple to complex forms. One is the energy of the sun which increases the number of relationships among simple units and helps to lift the single units over the energy limits in which they are embodied; and the second is natural selection which creates new levels of stability by favoring, through feedback, the development of more stable configurations. The more complex structures are built on the lower levels of functioning. Each ascending level denotes an increase in the capacity for patterns of interaction.

In the process of personality revolution, the opening to new relationships and new patterns of relating provides an energy similar to that provided by the sun.

Although it is mysterious, we can document by observation the fact that real change occurs every time we open to the intimacy and immediacy of being with another person. We feel a difference, we care and that is a difference which makes a difference. It is a distinction in the concrete here and now, and, suddenly, we are open to other feelings about other people and ourselves. This was one of the great insights of Freud's understanding of transference in psychoanalysis. When a patient sees the actual way he feels with his analyst, there can be an opening to the entire process of how he feels with all people. He recognizes his fears of other people in a setting where there is some "hope" that he need not be so afraid. In this context, he can examine this fear of uncertainty about others.

A good psychoanalyst or a good friend is one who encourages the wider dimensions of experiencing. By so doing, he supports the evolution to more complex and stable forms. Without such influences, there is a tendency for people to fall back to less demanding levels of being. The first move into the new forms is perhaps inevitably a terrible challenge. It is at these times that the friend or analyst provides the energy that natural selection provides by encouraging the individual to try. He may help the person in the resolution of the questions that arise. He may help him fit his new appreciation of wider relationships into other well-functioning systems. He may encourage participation in a group which will aid his growth. He may encourage work in an art as a system of value dedicated to the development of self. He may help in the opposition to forms which conspire to maintain inertia or the loss of autonomy. In whatever way, he is the assistant and aid for further elaboration of the evolution of the self.

The ultimate objective of the process is to understand the totality of the self's capacity for transforming; to appreciate the openness of connections and possible connecting which always are present; in fact, to discover that nature is a flow of ever-expanding relating processes of which every human being is an inevitable part.

References

REFERENCES: CHAPTER 1

1. Eckhard Hess, "Imprinting," *Science,* 130 (1959), 133.

2. R. Held and S.J. Friedman, "Plasticity and Human Sensorimotor Control," *Modern Systems Research for the Behavioral Scientist* (Chicago: Aldine, 1968).

3. Joseph Needham, *Order and Life* (Cambridge: MIT Press, 1968).

4. A. Lwoff, *Biological Order* (Cambridge: MIT Press, 1962), p. 9.

5. Alfred North Whitehead, *Process and Reality* (New York: Macmillan, a Free Press Paperback, 1969).

6. David Bohm, *Causality and Chance in Modern Physics* (1957; rpt. Philadelphia: University of Pennsylvania Press, 1971).

7. David Bohm, "Some Remarks on the Notion of Order," *Towards a Theoretical Biology,* ed. C.H. Waddington (Chicago: Aldine Publishing Co., 1969).

8. Harold Kelman, "A Phenomenologic Approach to Dream Interpretation," Part II, *The American Journal of Psychoanalysis,* 27 (1967), 75-94.

9. L.L. Whyte, A.G. Wilson, and D. Wilson, *Hierarchical Structures* (New York: American Elsevier Publishing Co., 1969).

10. Arthur Koestler and J.R. Smythies, *The Alpbach Symposium 1968: Beyond Reductionism* (New York: Macmillan, 1969).

11. Jean Piaget, *The Mechanisms of Perception* (New York: Basic Books, 1969).

12. J. Bruner, R.R. Oliver, and P.M. Greenfield, *Studies in Cognitive Growth* (New York: John Wiley, Inc., 1966).

13. Sigmund Freud, *The Interpretation of Dreams* (London, George Allen & Unwin, Ltd., 1954).

14. B. Apfelbaum, "Ego Psychology: Critique of the Structural Approach to Psychoanalytic Theory," *International Journal of Psychoanalysis,* 47 (1965), 451-475.

15. Pinchas Noy, "A Revision of the Psychoanalytic Theory of the Primary Process," *International Journal of Psychoanalysis,* 50 (1969), 155-177.

16. D. Yankelovich and W. Barrett, *Ego and Instinct: The Psychoanalytic View of Human Nature* (revised), (New York: Random House, 1970).

17. Silvano Arieti, *The Intrapsychic Self* (New York: Basic Books, 1967).

18. E. Galenson, "A Consideration of the Nature of Thought in Childhood Play," *Separation-Indurduation*, ed. J.B. McDevitt and C.F. Settlage (New York: International Universities Press, 1971).

19. Susanne Langer, *Philosophy in a New Key* (New York: Mentor Books, 1951).

20. L. Breger, "The Function of Dreams," *J. Abnor. Psychol: Psychological Monograph*, 72, No. 5, 1967.

21. George Klein, ref. to by P. Noy, ref. 15.

22. M. Merleau-Ponty, *The Structure of Behavior* (Boston: Beacon Press, 1963).

23. Emanual Peterfreund, "Information, Systems and Psychoanalysis: An Evolutionary Biological Approach to Psychoanalytic Theory," *Psychological Issues,* Vol. VII, Nos. 1/2, Monograph 25/26 (New York: International University Press, 1971).

24. Michael Polanyi, *Personal Knowledge* (Chicago: Chicago University Press, 1958).

25. J.Z. Young, *An Introduction to the Study of Man* (London: Oxford, 1972).

26. Gregory Bateson, *Steps to an Ecology of Mind* (New York: Ballatine Books, 1972).

27. J. Knshnamurti, *The Flight of the Eagle* (New York: Harper, 1971).

28. Jean Piaget, "Genetic Epistemology," *Columbia Forum,* Fall 1969, Vol. 12, 4-12.

29. John Platt, "The Two Faces of Perception," *Changing Perspectives on Man,* ed. B. Rothblatt (Chicago: University of Chicago Press, 1968).

Miscellaneous

Walter M. Elsasser, *Atom and Organism* (Princeton: Princeton University Press, 1966).

Martin Heidegger, *What is a Thing* (Chicago: Henry Regnery Co., 1967).

Heidegger, *What is Thinking* (New York: Harper, 1968).

Heidegger, *Discourse on Thinking* (New York: Harper, 1967).

Peter H. Knapp, "Image, Symbol, and Person: The Strategy of Psychological Defense," *Arch. General Psychiatry,* 21 (1969), 392-405.

Jean Piaget, *Structuralism* (New York: Basic Books, 1969).

REFERENCES: CHAPTER 2

1. Harold Kelman, "Toward a Definition of Mind," in *Theories of the Mind,* ed. J. Scher (New York: Free Press of Glencoe, 1962).
2. H. Ellenberger, *The Discovery of the Unconscious* (New York: Basic Books, 1970).
3. R. Holt, A Review of Some of Freud's Biological Assumptions and Their Influences on His Theories, in *Psychoanalysis and Current Biological Thought*, ed. N.S. Greenfield and W.C. Lewis (Madison and Milwaukee: University of Wisconsin Press, 1965).
4. *Ibid.,* p. 95
5. *Loc. cit.*
6. *Loc. cit.*
7. *Ibid.,* p. 98.
8. *Ibid.,* p. 99.
9. *Ibid.,* p. 104.
10. *Ibid.,* p. 106.
11. C.S. Pittendrigh, "Circadian Rhythms and the Circadian Organization of Living Systems," *Quart. Biol.,* 25 (1960), 159-173.
12. K.H. Pribram, *Languages of the Brain* (Englewood Cliffs, New Jersey: Prentice-Hall, 1971).
13. T.H. Bullock, "Neuron Doctrine and Electrophysiology," *Science,* 129 (1959), 997-1002.
14. H.W. Magoun, *The Waking Brain* (Springfield: Charles & Thomas, 1958).
15. J.C. Eccles, *Facing Reality* (New York: Springer Verlag, 1970).
16. Pribram, *op. cit.*
17. M. Merleau-Ponty, *The Structure of Behavior* (Boston: Beacon PB 266, 1963).
18. K. Goldstein, *The Organism* (New York: American Book Co., 1939).
19. David Bohm, "Human Nature as the Product of Our Mental Models," a talk delivered at the Institute of Contemporary Arts, London, England.
20. K.H. Pribram, *op. cit.,* chapter one.
21. Quoted in Pribram, *op. cit.,* p. 23.
22. Gunther Stent, "Cellular Communication," *Scientific American,* 227 (1972), 42-51.
23. H.B. Barlow, R. Narasimhan, and A. Rosenfeld, "Visual Pattern and Animals," *Science,* 177 (1972), 567-575.
24. J.Y. Lettvin, H.R. Maturana, W.S. McCulloch, and W.H. Pitts, "What the Frog's Eye Tells the Frog's Brain," *Proceedings of the Institute of Radio Engineers,* 47 (1959), 1940-51.
25. J.D. Pettigrew, "The Neurophysiology of Binocular Vision," *Scientific American,* 227 (1972), 84-96.

26. A. Roe and G.G. Simpson, *Behavior and Evolution* (New Haven: Yale University Press, 1958).
27. H.V.B. Hirsch and D.N. Spinelli, "Visual Experience Modified Distribution of Horizontally and Vertically Oriented Receptive Fields in Cats," *Science*, 168, (1970), 869.
28. J. Platt, "The Two Faces of Perception," in *Changing Perspectives on Man*, ed. B. Rothblatt (Chicago: University of Chicago Press, 1968).
29. D. Hebb, *The Organization of Behavior* (New York: Wiley, 1949).
30. Platt, *op. cit.*
31. K.S. Lashley, "The Problem of Serial Order in Behavior," in *Psycholinguistics: A Book of Readings*, ed. S. Saporta and J.R. Bastian (New York: Holt, Rinehart & Winston, 1966).
32. K.H. Pribram, "The Neurophysiology of Remembering," *Scientific American*, 220 (1969), 73.
33. Pribram, *ibid.*
34. Henry Beck, "Minimal Requirements for a Biobehavioral Paradigm," *Behav. Science*, 16 (1971), 442-455.
35. G.A. Miller, E. Galenter, and K.H. Pribram, *Plans and the Structure of Behavior* (New York: Holt & Co., 1960).
36. N. Bernstein, *The Coordination and Regulation of Movements* (Long Island City, New York: Pergamon Press, 1967), p. 133.
37. J. Bruner, "On Perceptual Readiness," *Psychological Review*, 64 (1957), 123-152.
38. K.H. Pribram, *Languages of the Brain* (Englewood Cliffs, New Jersey: Prentice-Hall, 1971).
39. E.N. Sokolov, "Higher Nervous Functions, The Orienting Reflex," *Annual Review of Physiology*, 25 (1963), 545.
40. K.H. Pribram, *ibid.*
41. Thomas H. Kuhn, *The Structure of Scientific Revolutions* (Chicago: University of Chicago Press, 1964).
42. George Mandler and David L. Watson, "Anxiety and the Interruption of Behavior," in *Anxiety and Behavior*, ed. Charles Spielberger (New York: Academic Press, 1966).
43. S. Schachter, "The Interaction of Cognitive and Physiological Determinants of Emotional State," in *Anxiety and Behavior*, ed. Charles Spielberger (New York: Academic Press, 1966).
44. Akira Kasamatsu and Tomio Hirai, "An Electroencephalographic Study of the Zen Meditation (Zazen)," in *Biofeedback and Self Control: An Aldine Reader of the Regulation of Bodily Processes and Consciousness*, ed. T. Barber, L.V. Dicara, J. Kamiya, N. Miller, and J. Stoyva (Chicago: Aldine-Atherton, 1971).

REFERENCES: CHAPTER 3

1. Kurt Goldstein, "The Organismic Approach," in *The American Handbook of Psychiatry*, Vol. II, ed. Silvano Arieti (New York: Basic Books, 1959).
2. Karen Horney, *Neurosis and Human Growth* (New York: Norton, 1950).
3. H. Kelman, *Helping People* (New York: Science House, 1971).
4. G. Mandler and D.L. Watson, "Anxiety and the Interruption of Behavior," in *Anxiety and Behavior*, ed. Charles D. Spielberger (New York: Academic Press, 1966).
5. Jay M. Weiss, "Psychological Factors in Stress and Disease," *Scientific American*, 226 (1972), 104-112.
6. David Shapiro, *Neurotic Styles* (New York: Basic Books, 1965).
7. G.A. Miller, E. Galenter, and K.H. Pribram, *Plans and the Structure of Behavior* (New York: Holt & Co., 1960).

8. J. Haley, "The Family of the Schizophrenic: A Model System," *Journal Nerv. and Mental Disease,* 129 (1959), 357.

9. Theodore Lidz, A. Cornelison, D. Jerry, and Stephen Fleck, "Interfamilial Environment of the Schizophrenic Patient," VI, "The Transmission of Irrationality," *AMA Archives of Neurology and Psychology,* 79 (1958), 305.

10. M.R. Singer, L.C. Wynne, "Family Transactions and Schizophrenia," *The Origins of Schizophrenia,* ed. John Romano (New York: Excerpta Medica Foundation International Congress Series, No. 151, 1967).

11. J.H. Weakland, "The Double Bind Hypothesis of Schizophrenia and Three Party Interaction," *The Etiology of Schizophrenia,* ed. D.D. Jackson (New York: Basic Books, 1960).

12. R.D. Laing, *The Politics of Experience* (New York: Pantheon, 1967), p. 114.

13. David Shainberg, "Neuropsychologic Guides to Psychoanalytic Technique," *American Journal of Psychotherapy,* 25 (1971), 458.

14. C.S. Pittendrigh, "Adaptation, Natural Selection and Behavior," in *Behavior and Evolution,* ed. A. Roe and G.G. Simpson (New Haven: Yale University Press, 1958).

REFERENCES: CHAPTER 4

1. Silvano Arieti, "Schizophrenia: The Manifest Symptomotology, the Psychodynamic and Formal Mechanism," in *The American Handbook of Psychiatry,* Chap. 23-24 (New York: Basic Books, 1959).

2. David Shakow, "Some Psychological Aspects of Schizophrenia," in *The Origins of Schizophrenia,* ed. J. Romano (New York: Excerpta Medica Foundation, 1967).

3. R.D. Laing, *The Divided Self* (London: Tavistock Publications, 1960).

4. R.D. Laing, *The Self and Others* (Baltimore: Penguin Books, 1969).

5. D. Bannister and F. Fransella, *Inquiring Man: The Theory of Personal Constructs* (Baltimore, Penguin Books, 1971).

6. George Kelly, *A Theory of Personality: The Psychology of Personal Constructs,* (New York: Norton, 1963).

7. The discussions here arranged from David Shainberg, "The Dilemma and the Challenge of Being Schizophrenic," presented at the Annual Meeting of the American Academy of Psychoanalysis, Dallas, Texas, 1972; to be published in the *Journal of the American Academy of Psychoanalysis*, Vol. 1, 1973.

8. Julian Silverman, "Shamans and Acute Schizophrenia," *American Anthropologist,* 69 (1967), 21-33.

9. William L. Pious, "Hypothesis about the Nature of Schizophrenic Behavior," in *Psychotherapy of the Psychoses,* ed. Arthur Burten (New York: Basic Books, 1961).

10. E. Schactel, "The Development of Focal Attention and the Emergence of Reality," in *Metamorphosis* (New York: Basic Books, 1959).

11. Edward M. Ornitz, "Disorders of Perception in Early Infantile Autism and Schizophrenia," *Comprehensive Psychiatry,* 10 (1969), 259-269.

12. Lara Jefferson, *The Inner World of Mental Illness,* ed. Bert Kaplan (New York: Harper, 1964), p. 11.

13. H. Ellenberger, *The Discovery of the Unconscious* (New York: Basic Books, 1970).

14. J.M. Scher, "The Concept of Self," in *Chronic Schizophrenia,* ed. L. Appelby, J.M. Scher and John Cumming (New York: Free Press of Glencoe, 1960), pp. 149-174.

15. Malcolm B. Bowers, "Pathogenesis of Acute Schizophrenic Psychosis: An Experimental Approach," *Archives General Psychology,* 19 (1968), 348.

REFERENCES: CHAPTER 5

1. David Noton and L. Stark, "Eye Movements and Visual Perception," *Scientific American,* 224 (1971), 34-43.
2. I. Cooke and M. Lipkin, Jr., ed., *Papers in Cellular Neurophysiology* (New York: Holt, Rinehart & Winston, 1972).
3. H.A. Johnson, "Information Theory in Biology," *Science,* 168 (1970), 1545-1550.
4. James Miller, "Living Systems," *Basic Concepts of Behavioral Science,* 10 (1965), 193-237; *Structure and Process,* 10 (1965), 337-379.
5. H. Kelman, "Life History as Therapy," *American Journal of Psychoanalysis,* 16 (1956), 145-169.
6. David Shakow, "Some Psychophysiological Aspects of Schizophrenia," in *The Origins of Schizophrenia,* ed. J. Romano (New York: Excerpta Medica Foundation, 1967).
7. Elkes, quoted in Shakow, ref. 6.
8. H.G. Birch and M.E. Hertzig, "Etiology of Schizophrenia: An Overview of the Relation of Development to Atypical Behavior," in *The Origins of Schizophrenia,* ed. J. Romano (New York: Excerpta Medica Foundation, 1967).
9. Silvano Arieti, *The Intrapsychic Self* (New York: Basic Books, 1969).
10. Lev. S. Vygotsky, *Thought and Language* (Cambridge: MIT Press, 1962).
11. Jean Piaget and Barbel Inhelder, "The Gaps in Empiricism," in *Beyond Reductionism,* ed. Arthur Koestler (New York: Macmillan, 1969).
12. David McNeil, *The Acquisition of Language: The Study of Developmental Linguistics* (New York: Harper & Row, 1970).
13. Susan Ervin, "Imitation and Structural Change in Children's Language," in *New Directions in the Study of Language,* ed., E.H. Lenneberg (Cambridge: MIT Press, 1964).
14. H. Shands, *The War with Words* (The Hague: Mouton, 1971).
15. David H. Hubel, "Effects of Distortion of Sensory Input on the Visual Systems of Kittens," Eleventh Bowditch Lecture, *The Physiologist,* 10 (1967), 17.
16. Helmut V.B. Hirsch and D.N. Spinelli, "Visual Experience Modified Distribution of Horizontally and Vertically Oriented Receptive Fields in Cats,." *Science,* 168 (1970), 869.
17. Jack Hailman, "How an Instinct Is Learned," *Scientific American,* 221 (1969), 98-108.
18. David Shakow, "Understanding Normal Psychological Function: Contributions from Schizophrenia," *Arch. Gen. Psych.,* 17 (1967), 306.
19. E.H. Rodnick, "Cognitive and Perceptual Response Set in Schizophrenics in Cognition," in *Personality and Clinical Psychology,* ed. Richard Jesser and Seymour Feshbach (San Francisco: Jussey-Bass, Inc., 1968).
20. R.D. Laing, *The Politics of Experience* (New York: Pantheon, 1967).
21. Barbara O'Brien, *Operators and Things* (New York: Ace Books, 1957).
22. Karen Horney, "Finding the Real Self: A Letter with a Foreword by Karen Horney,". *American Journal of Psychoanalysis,* 9 (1949), 3.
23. Richard M. Bucke, *Cosmic Consciousness: A Study in the Evolution of the Human Mind* (1901; rpt. New York: E.P. Dutton, 1923).
24. R.D. Laing, *The Politics of the Family,* Massey Lectures, 1968 (Toronto: CBC Publications, 1969).
25. Anton Boisen, quoted in *Varieties of Psychopathological Experience* by Carney Landis, ed. Fred A. Mettler (New York: Holt, Rinehart & Winston, 1964), p. 101.
26. B. Ghiselin, ed. *The Creative Process* (New York: New American Library, 1952).
27. Jordan Scher, "Mind as Participation," in *Theories of the Mind,* ed. Jordan Scher (New York: The Free Press of Glencoe, 1962).
28. John S. Kafka, "Ambiguity for Individuation: A Critique and Reformation of Double Bind Theory," *Archives Gen. Psych.,* 25 (1971), 232-239.

29. K.E. Hite, "A Phenomenon of Rebirth: Coming Alive in Analytic and Medical Patients," *American Journal of Psychoanalysis,* 30 (1968), 19-29.

30. A.H. Maslow, *Toward a Psychology of Being* (New York: D. Van Nostrand, 1962).

31. Harold Kelman, "Kairos: The Auspicious Moment," *American Journal of Psychoanalysis,* 29 (1969), 59-83.

32. Erik Erikson, *Childhood and Society* (New York: W.W. Norton, 1963).

33. Harold Kelman, *Helping People* (New York: Science House, 1971).

34. Harold Kelman, "Communing and Relating," *American Journal of Psychoanalysis,* 18 (1958), 77-98, 158-170; 19 (1959), 73-105,188-215.

35. M. Balint, *The Basic Fault: Therapeutic Aspects of Regression* (London: Tavistock, 1967).

36. David Shainberg, "Structure and Ground," an unpublished manuscript.

37. Morag Coate, *Beyond All Reason* (New York: Lippincott, 1965).

38. W.W. Meissner, "The Temporal Dimension in the Understanding of Human Experience," *Journal of Existentialism,* 7 (1965), 129-158.

39. E. Minkowski, *Lived Time: Phenomenological and Psychopathological Studies,* trans N. Metzel (Evanston: Northwestern University Press, 1972).

40. *Op. cit.* Coate (ref. 37), p. 29.

41. E.R. Sinnett, *The Diary of a Schizophrenic Man*, quoted in *The Inner World of Mental Illness.* ed. B. Kaplan, p. 186 (New York: Harper & Row, 1964).

REFERENCES: CHAPTER 6

1. Thomas Kuhn, "The Structure of Scientific Revolutions," in *The International Encyclopedia of Unified Science,* Vol. II, #2 (Chicago: University of Chicago Press, 1962).

2. F.T. Melges and T. Bowlby, "Types of Hopelessness in Psychopathological Process," *Arch. Gen. Psych.* 20 (1969), 690.

3. Karen Horney, "Finding the Real Self: A Letter with a Foreword by Karen Horney," *American Journal of Psychoanalysis,* 9 (1949), 3.

4. Hannah Green, *I Never Promised You a Rose Garden* (New York: Signet Book, New American Library, 1964).

5. John Perceval, *Perceval's Narrative: A Patient's Account of his Psychosis,* ed. Gregory Bateson (Stanford: Stanford University Press, 1961).

REFERENCES: CHAPTER 7

1. M.S. Palazzoli, "Anorexia Nervosa," in *The World Biennial of Psychiatry and Psychotherapy,* ed. Silvano Arieti (New York: Basic Books, 1970).

2. Harold Searles, "The Differentiation between Concrete and Metaphorical Thinking in the Recovering Schizophrenic Patient," in *Collected Papers on Schizophrenia and Related Subjects* (New York: International Universities Press, 1965).

3. Carney Landis, *Varieties of Psychopathological Experience,* ed. Fred A. Mettler (New York: Holt, Rinehart & Winston, 1962).

4. J. Lang, "The Other Side of Hallucinations," *American Journal of Psychoanal.,* 96 (1939), 423-433.

5. Sigmund Freud, *An Outline of Psychoanalysis* (New York: W.W. Norton & Co., 1949).

6. Landis, *op. cit.*

7. David Shakow, "Understanding Normal Psychological Function, Contributions from Schizophrenia," *Arch. Gen. Psychiatry,* 17 (1967), 306.

8. M. Bleuler, *Dementia Praecox or the Group of Schizophrenias* (New York: International University Press, 1950).

9. V. Zarcone, G. Gulevich, T. Picik, and William Dement, "Partial REM Phase Deprivation and Schizophrenia," *Arch. Gen. Psych.*, 18 (1968), 194.

10. G. Vailliant, "Prospective Prediction of Schizophrenic Remission," *Arch. Gen. Psych.*, 11 (1964), 509.

11. Jack Rubins, "Psychodynamics and Psychosomatic Symptoms," *The American Journal of Psychoanal.*, 19 (1959), 165.

12. Alexander Reid Martin, "The Body's Participation in Dilemma and Anxiety Phenomena," in *Advances in Psychoanalysis*, ed. H. Kelman (New York: W.W. Norton & Co., 1964).

13. Schreber, quoted in Landis, *op. cit.* (ref. 3), p. 56.

14. Alfred North Whitehead, *Science and the Modern World* (New York: The Free Press, 1967).

15. R.D. Laing, *The Politics of Experience* (New York: Pantheon, 1967).

16. McCall, quoted in Landis, p. 251.

17. M. Sechehaye, *Autobiography of a Schizophrenic Girl* (New York: Grune and Stratton, 1951).

18. Hannah Green, *I Never Promised You a Rose Garden* (New York: Signet, New American Library, 1964).

19. Morag Coate, *Beyond All Reason* (New York: Lippincott, 1965).

20. David Cooper, *Psychiatry and Anti-Psychiatry* (London: Tavistock, 1967), p. 28.

21. M. Eliade, *Shamanism* (New York: Pantheon, 1964).

22. I.M. Lewis, *Ecstatic Religion: An Anthropological Study of Spirit Possession and Shamanism* (Baltimore: Penguin, 1971).

REFERENCES: CHAPTER 8

1. Paul Hackett, *The Cardboard Giants* (New York: G.P. Putnam, 1952).

2. Barbara O'Brien, *Operators and Things* (New York: Ace Books, 1958).

3. D. Winnicott, quoted by Peter Lomas, "Passivity and Failure of Identity Development," *International Journal of Psychoanalysis*, 46 (1965), 438.

4. K.R. Eissler, "Remarks on the Psychoanalysis of Schizophrenia," *International Journal of Psychoanalysis*, 32 (1951), 139.

5. Malcolm Bowers and B. Astrachan, "Depression in Acute Schizophrenic Psychosis," *Am. J. Psychiatry*, 123 (1967), 974.

6. Sheldon Roth, "The Seemingly Ubiquitous Depression Following Acute Schizophrenic Episodes; A Neglected Area of Clinical Discussion," *Am. J. Psychiatry*, 127 (1970), 91.

7. G. Vailliant, "Prospective Prediction of Schizophrenic Remission," *Arch. Gen. Psych.*, 11 (1964), 509.

8. S. Sonnenberg and Jean B. Miller, Paper presented at Annual Meeting of the American Academy of Psychoanalysis, May 1972, to be published in *Journal Am. Acad. of Psychoanalysis.*

REFERENCES: CHAPTER 9

1. Paul Federn, "The Ego in Schizophrenia," in *Ego Psychology and the Psychoses*, ed. Eduardo Weiss (New York: Basic Books, 1952).

2. Louis Breger, Ian Hunter, and Ron W. Lane, "The Effect of Stress on Dreams, *Psych. Issues*, Vol. 7, Mono 27, Int. University Press, 1971.

3. J.B. Miller, "Waking and Dreaming Conceptualization in Depression," in *Depressions: Theories and Therapies*, ed. J. Masserman, Vol. XVII of *Science and Psychoanalysis* (New York: Grune and Stratton, 1970).

4. H. Rennert, referred to in Roland Fischer, "A Cartography of the Ecstatic and Meditative States, *Science,* 174 (1971), 897-904.

5. Otto Billig, "Structures of Schizophrenic Forms of Expression," *Psych. Quarterly,* 44 (1970), 187-222.

6. Hannah Green, *I Never Promised You a Rose Garden* (New York: New American Library, 1964).

7. H.M. Voth, A.C. Voth, and R. Cancro, "Suicidal Solution as a Function of Ego Closeness," *Arch. Gen. Psych.,* 21 (1969), 536-545.

8. Carney Landis, *Varieties of Psychopathological Experience,* ed. Fred A. Mettler (New York: Holt, Rinehart & Winston, 1962).

9. Quoted in Julian Silverman, "When Schizophrenia Helps," *Psychology Today,* 4 (1970), 62.

10. A. Boisen, quoted in Landis, ref. 8.

11. J. Scher, "The Concept of Self," in *Chronic Schizophrenia,* ed. L. Appleby, J.M. Scher, John Cumming (New York: Free Press of Glencoe, 1960).

12. Silvano Arieti, *The Intrapsychic Self* (New York: Basic Books, 1967).

13. Harold Kelman, "Communing and Relating," *American Journal of Psychoanalysis,* 18 (1958), 77-98, 158-170; 19 (1959) 73-105, 188-215.

REFERENCES: CHAPTER 10

1. Jurgen Ruesch and Gregory Bateson, *Communication: The Social Matrix of Psychiatry* (New York: Norton, 1968).

2. J. Scher, "Mind as Participation," in *Theories of the Mind,* ed. J. Scher (New York: Free Press of Glencoe, 1962).

3. Francis Macnaab, *Estrangement and Relationship: Experience with Schizophrenics* (Bloomington: Indiana University Press, 1966).

4. Jean Piaget, *Psychology and Epistemology: Toward a Theory of Knowledge,* trans. Arnold Rasin (New York: Orian Press Book, Grossman, 1971).

5. Silvano Arieti, *The Intrapsychic Self: Feeling, Cognition and Creativity in Health and Mental Illness* (New York: Basic Books, 1967).

6. Ernst Cassirer, "The Philosophy of Symbolic Forms," Vol. 2, *Mythical Thought,* Yale Paper (New Haven: Yale University Press, 1955).

7. John S. Kafka, "Ambiguity for Individuation, A Critique and Reformation of Double Bind Theory," *Archives of Psychiatry,* 25 (1971), 232-239.

8. Howard I. Levene, "Acute Schizophrenia: Clinical Effects of the Labeling Process," *Arch. Gen. Psych.,* 25 (1971), 215.

REFERENCES: CHAPTER 11

1. Morag Coate, *Beyond All Reason* (New York: Lippincott, 1965).

2. Gordon G. Gallup, "The Mirror of the Mind," *The New Scientist,* rpt. in *Intellectual Digest,* April 1972.

3. R.D. Laing, *The Divided Self* (London: Tavistock Publication, 1960).

4. Hannah Green, *I Never Promised You a Rose Garden* (New York: New American Library, 1964).

5. Coate, *op. cit.*

6. P. Elkish, "The Psychological Significance of the Mirror," *Journal of the American Psychoan. Assoc.,* 5 (1957), 235.

7. Karen Horney, *New Ways in Psychoanalysis* (New York: W.W. Norton, 1939).

8. James Frazer, *The Golden Bough* (New York: Macmillan Co., 1948).

9. Malcolm Bowers, "The Onset of Psychosis: A Diary Account," *Psychiatry,* 28 (1965) 346.

10. J. Perceval, *Perceval's Narrative, A Patient's Account of his Psychosis,* ed. Gregory ateson (Stanford: Stanford University Press, 1961).
11. J.S. Bruner, Rose R. Oliver, and Patricia Greenfield, *Studies in Cognitive Growth,* Jew York: John Wiley, 1966).
12. Jean Piaget, *Psychology and Epistemology: Toward a Theory of Knowledge,* trans. rnold Rasin (New York: Orian Press Book, Grossman, 1971).
13. Sibylle Escalona, *The Roots of Individuality* (Chicago: Aldine, 1968).
14. René A. Spitz, *The First Year of Life* (New York: International Universities Press, 965).
15. Sylvia Brody and Sidney Axelrod, *Anxiety and Ego Formation in Infancy* (New ork: International Universities Press, 1970).
16. Bruner, et al., *op. cit.*
17. Carney Landis, *Varieties of Psychopathological Experience,* ed. Fred Mettler (New ork: Holt, Rinehart, & Winston, 1965).
18. Arranged from David Shainberg, "Neuropsychological Guides to Psychoanalytic echnique," *American Journal of Psychotherapy,* 25 (1971), 458-468.

REFERENCES: CHAPTER 12

1. Thomas Kuhn, "The Structure of Scientific Revolutions," in *International Encyclodia of Unified Science,* Vol. II, no. 2 (Chicago: University of Chicago Press, 1962).
2. Ervin Laszlo, *The Systems View of the World* (New York: Braziller, 1972).
3. Harold Kelman, *Helping People* (New York: Science House, 1971).
4. Karen Horney, "Finding the Real Self: A Letter with a Foreword by Karen Horney," *merican Journal of Psychoanalysis,* 9 (1949), 3.

REFERENCES: CHAPTER 13

1. Bob Dylan, "Just Like a Woman," (New York: Columbia Records, album, "Blonde on onde," issued May 1966).
2. Bob Dylan, *op. cit.*
3. D. Winnicott, "Ego Distortion in Terms of True and False Self," in *The Maturational ocesses and the Facilitating Environment* (London: Hogarth, 1965).
4. Jean Piaget, *The Mechanisms of Perception* (New York: Basic Books, 1969).
5. J. Bruner, R. Oliver, P. Greenfield, *Studies in Cognitive Growth* (New York: John iley, 1966).
6. Bruner et al., *op. cit.* p. 53.
7. *Ibid.*, p. 54.
8. Harold Kelman, *Helping People* (New York: Science House, 1971), p. 405.
9. Harold Kelman, "Life History as Therapy," *American Journal of Psychoanalysis*, 16 956), 145.
10. J.E. Dyrud and Charles Donnelly, "Executive Functions of the Ego," *Arch. Gen. ychiatry*, 20 (1969), 257.
11. Sara Sheiner, "An Investigation of a Learning Block in Schizophrenia," *American urnal of Psychoanalysis*, 30 (1969), 205-211.
12. Sara Sheiner, "Intensity of Casual Relationships in Schizophrenia: Living in agination," *American Journal of Psychoanalysis*, 28 (1968), 156.
13. Eleanor Galenson, "A Consideration of the Nature of Thought in Childhood Play," in *paration-Individuation: Essays in Honor of Margaret S. Mahler*, ed. J.B. McDevitt and C.F. ttlage (New York: International University Press, 1971).
14. Bruner et al., *op. cit.*, p. 45.

REFERENCES: CHAPTER 14

1. David Shainberg, "Personality Restriction in Adolescence," *Psych. Quarterly*, 4 (1966), 258.
2. Harold Kelman, *Helping People* (New York: Science House, 1971).
3. J. Wallingá, "Adolescent Auto Theft," *Journal of the American Academy of Chi Psychiatrists*, 3 (1964), 126.
4. Douglas D. Bond, *The Love and Fear of Flying* (New York: International Universit Press, 1952).
5. Erik Erikson, *Childhood and Society* (New York: Norton, 1950).
6. Jean Piaget, *The Psychology of Intelligence* (London: Routledge and Keegan Pau 1960).
7. John Flavell, *The Developmental Psychology of Jean Piaget* (Princeton: Van Nostran 1962).
8. H. Nash, "The Role of Metaphor in Psychological Theory," *Behavioral Science*, (1963), 336.

REFERENCES: CHAPTER 15

1. Morag Coate, *Beyond All Reason* (New York: Lippincott, 1965).
2. Kazimierz Dabrowski, "Personality Shaping through Positive Disintegration" (Bosto Little, Brown, 1967).
3. Susanne Langer, *Mind: An Essay on Human Feeling*, Vol. I (Baltimore: John Hopki University Press, 1967), p. 310.
4. Herbert A. Simon, *The Sciences of the Artificial* (Cambridge: MIT Press, 1969).
5. John Platt, "Hierarchical Growth," *Bulletin of the Atomic Scientists*, November 197
6. Ervin Laszlo, *The Systems View of the World* (New York: Braziller, 1972).
7. J. Bronowski, "New Concepts in the Evolution of Complexity: Stratified Stability ar Unbounded Plans," *Synthese*, 21 (1970), 228-246.

Index